Depression

A Practical Guide to Coping

C.A.H. Watts
OBE, MD, FRCGP, FRCPsych,
D(Obst)RCOG

The Crowood Press

First published in 1989 by
The Crowood Press
Ramsbury, Marlborough,
Wiltshire SN8 2HE

British Library Cataloguing in Publication Data

Watts, Arthur
Depression: a practical guide to coping.
1. Man. Depression. Therapy. Self-help, –
Manuals
I. Title
616.85′2706

ISBN 1 85223 132 7

Dedicated to my wife Betty

Line illustrations by Sharon Perks

Typset by Inforum Typesetting, Portsmouth
Printed in Great Britain by MacLehose & Partners Ltd, Portsmouth

Contents

1
What is Depression?

By undertaking to read this book, you have shown an interest in mental depression. This condition is one of the commonest and most distressing afflictions known to mankind, yet it is often misunderstood by the public at large. There must be few families who have not suffered a casualty of this nature, yet the man in the street often has little time or sympathy for the depressed person and there are still a few doctors and other professionals who don't really understand this common malady.

Many people suffering from this illness don't realise that they are indeed sick, and they can be misunderstood by both relatives and friends. Some people who have been victims of this disorder assert that only another person who has suffered from the illness can appreciate the full horror of the condition, and there is some truth in this. All this ignorance and apathy about a common malady is a great pity, as today, *depression is a treatable disease*. Learning more about depression could well be your first step towards recovery in yourself, or in some relative you feel is suffering from the condition.

A bad depression is the most intense agony known to man. The old name for the disease was 'melancholia', and in its most severe form, it has been recognised and well documented as an illness, throughout history. This gross form of depression is certainly not likely to elude detection. The sick person is so obviously disturbed that the family invariably seeks expert advice, and the patient gets the appropriate treatment. However, the most alarming manifestations are comparatively rare. It is the mild and moderate forms of the illness that are often overlooked or misdiagnosed, but it must be emphasised that even a mild episode of depression can be a devastating experience. It is certainly no minor malady.

If you are depressed, you are in very good company, as many clever and famous people have been afflicted with the condition. David, the King of Israel, suffered from this illness, and in some of his psalms he gave a vivid description as to how he felt, abandoned by God and man.

'My God, my God, why hast thou forsaken me?
But as for me, I am a worm and no man;
A very scorn of men, an outcast of the people.
I am poured out like water, and all my bones are out of joint:
My heart also in the midst of my body is like melting wax.
My strength is dried up like a potsherd,
And my tongue cleaveth to my gums.   (*22nd Psalm*)

I am weary of my groaning,
Every night I flood my bed with my tears.   (*6th Psalm*)

I am desolate and in misery.'   (*25th Psalm*)

Many of these sentiments are repeated again and again by melancholics. Self depreciation, utter loneliness, and tears shed, are all such common symptoms. The patient who said that there was nothing wrong with her organs, but that it was what held her together that was missing, was in fact reiterating what the psalmist had to say about all his bones being out of joint.

For every unmistakable case of severe depression, there are many milder forms that go unrecognised and untreated, and the sufferers of these forms of depression are the people that this book aims to help. It is only since the end of the Second World War that these milder forms of melancholia have been accepted for what they are by the medical profession. Before then, such people were regarded as tiresome neurotics, feeble creatures putting on an act in an attempt to draw attention to themselves, or even as malingerers. Furthermore, the unhappy patient often received little sympathy from either family or friends, who were inclined to tell the sick person to pull himself together. Of course, it must be said that before there was any effective treatment for the condition, the correct diagnosis was not as important as it is today. If a doctor did diagnose a depression fifty years ago, there was little he could do about it beyond kindly supportive treatment, and a constant reassurance that the phase would pass, but few would be prepared to spend much time on such an unrewarding type of patient. Most family doctors had no idea that there was such a disease entity as a mild depression. This ignorance about the very existence of the condition by the medical profession is the more surprising because there have always been a few observant people who recognised the malady, including William Shakespeare who, in *The Merchant of Venice*, gave an accurate account of how the merchant, Antonio, felt as a mildly depressed person. Antonio was not slumped in the depths of melancholia and he didn't even claim to be ill. He was a successful business man, still active in his profession. This is how he described his feelings in the opening lines of the play.

'In sooth, I know not why I am so sad:
It wearies me; you say it wearies you;
But how I caught it, found it, or came by it,
What stuff 'tis made of, whereof it is born,
I am to learn;
And such a want-wit sadness makes of me,
That I have much ado to know myself.'

The last phrase, 'I just cannot understand myself', is echoed by many depressed people. The whole picture is typical, with the patient presenting an image of sadness and frustration. He is utterly perplexed by the situation.

In a monograph I wrote on depressive disorders (C.A.H. Watts, *Depressive Disorders in the Community* (John Wright, Bristol, 1966)), based on my own work and that of other investigators, I drew up a diagrammatic iceberg, depicting the size of the problem. This is reproduced below.

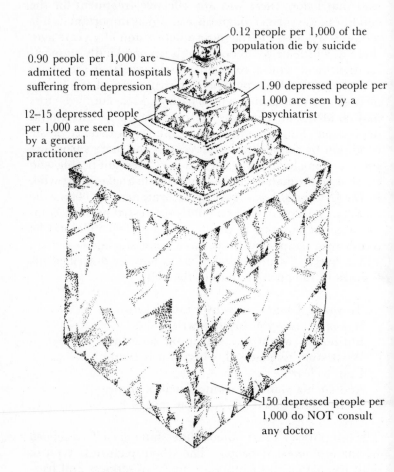

0.12 people per 1,000 of the population die by suicide

0.90 people per 1,000 are admitted to mental hospitals suffering from depression

1.90 depressed people per 1,000 are seen by a psychiatrist

12–15 depressed people per 1,000 are seen by a general practitioner

150 depressed people per 1,000 do NOT consult any doctor

The iceberg of depression.

This shows how many cases go unrecognised by all and sundry. The large reservoir of 150 persons per 1,000 includes vast numbers of the everyday type of misery that everyone experiences from time to time, but also includes a few severe cases in urgent need of treatment. These figures have generally been accepted by the profession as a rough measure of the size of the problem. Something like one in ten of the population can expect to suffer from a significant depressive reaction during their lifetime. These figures show that a depressive illness is a very common problem.

Throughout history famous characters have, from time to time, sunk into the slough of despond. Cowper the poet, Goya the painter, and Tchaikovsky the composer, all suffered from episodes of depression which were at times clearly depicted in their work. The brilliant Huxley family have been plagued with the condition, and Winston Churchill complained about his 'black dog', as he called such bad patches. This illness occurs in all races in every part of the world, afflicting rich and poor alike. Even royalty is not immune. George III had a sorry time at the hands of his physicians and the attendants in charge of his august person.

Given time, a depressive episode almost invariably passes but its average duration is about a year, over which period both the patient and his family suffer greatly. Before 1940 there was virtually no treatment known to cut short the agony, but things are very different today. As has already been said, *depression is now a treatable illness*, and within days of starting on the correct remedy, the black clouds of depression begin to disperse. No one should have to put up with depression either in themselves or in a relative. Nowadays family doctors are well aware of this trouble and know how to treat it, so seeking help from an expert very soon brings the misery to an end. If you are suffering from a depression, you may find it hard to believe such good news, but don't be put off. Even the most severe types of melancholia respond well to treatment.

2
Symptoms and their Consequences

One definition of depression is an inexplicable falling off of mental and physical energy to the point of distress. I have already pointed out that this condition is a most unpleasant one, and there are a number of reasons why this is so. The list of distressing symptoms that follows does not apply to each and every melancholic, but the deeper the depression, the more likely they are to be present.

A COMPLETE LACK OF HOPE

Not only is the mental anguish supreme, but at the same time the patient is completely devoid of hope; there is no light at the end of a long dark tunnel. This conviction that the future looks empty and futile is a symptom peculiar to a depression and doesn't occur in other forms of illness.

The man who has had a heart attack may well feel that 'the writing is on the wall', but he still hopes he will get better, and makes all sorts of good resolutions as to how, in the future, he will take things easier, stop smoking, and cut down on what he eats. He has every faith that the doctors will cure him. Even with a feared disease like cancer, there is always some hope. The patient feels that with luck the surgeon will be able to excise the growth completely, or that it may disappear with modern drug treatment. Furthermore, with every month that passes, there is always the chance that some new discovery may solve his problem.

The melancholic can derive no such comfort; he is com-

pletely convinced he is doomed, and
ance. He is sure that to consult a doct
time as there can be no remedy for

FEELINGS OF

Besides lack of hope, the patient r
some way responsible for his condition. A m...
that his troubles were all due to an attack of gonorrhoea ne
had had in his youth. Neither his family nor his friends had
any idea of this awful secret. He brooded with horror on how
they would react if they ever heard about it. A woman with a
family of three had been happily married for some twenty
years when she suffered from her first depression. She
blamed it all on the fact that she had been content to be
wedded in a registry office when she was a Catholic. Until
she had become melancholic, the marriage situation had
been no problem to her, but now she realised with disgust,
that for all these years, she had been living in sin.

Under normal circumstances, if we make a mistake, we
can find some extenuating circumstances, or someone else to
blame for what has happened. This doesn't happen in the
court of conscience, where at the same time one is the
prisoner in the dock as well as the judge and jury, and there is
no escape from painful condemnation. The guilt feelings in a
depression can be quite overwhelming. Custance described
how he felt at the bottom of the abyss in *Wisdom, Madness and
Folly* (Gollancz, London, 1951).

'I had by now become quite convinced that I was
finished for good and all. In fact though not dead, I was
as good as dead. Perhaps because I had committed
"the unforgivable sin" or just because I was such an
appalling sinner, the worst man that ever existed, I had
been chosen to go through the portals of Hell alive. It

ously too late for repentance; there was no
a reprieve; and that was the end of it.'

omplete this cocktail of horror, both the feelings of
pelessness and guilt are compounded by the apparently
slow passage of time. In a depression every minute can seem
like an hour.

In spite of all these feelings, given time, an expert can often
put across to the patient that he is in fact ill, and suffering
from a well-understood malady. I was once asked to see a
youth of 23 who had refused to attend my surgery, because
he was quite sure that no one would be able to help him. He
knew he was doomed, and to consult me was going to be a
complete waste of his time and mine. I agreed to visit him in
his own home, and there I listened to his story. It was the
usual picture of misery painted by a melancholic. I spent an
hour or so with him; first I listened and then I explained to
him that he was in fact suffering from a well-understood
illness. I suggested that he had been misled by some of his
symptoms. When I had gone, he told his parents that to his
amazement, I had been able to describe how he felt, better
than he was able to himself. I had given him just a glimmer of
hope, and on the strength of this he accepted the treatment I
had offered him, and in a few weeks he was back to normal.

The depressed patient can be compared with a traveller in
a foreign land who has lost his way. To make matters worse,
night is coming on and there is a storm brewing. He feels
acutely worried and distressed. Suddenly he meets a man
who speaks his own language, who is able to guide the
traveller back on to the right road. The feeling of relief
experienced by such a person is similar to that of the
depressed patient who comes face to face with an understanding physician who can explain what is happening. In
spite of the conviction that he has no future, the patient is
able to detect understanding which usually induces him to
take the treatment offered. Sympathy and patience are never

wasted on a melancholic, although at the time the patient may seem to be uninterested and unappreciative. He may have no faith in the treatment on offer, but it will work in spite of all his misgivings.

THE FALLING OFF OF ENERGY

Usually the first symptom of the illness is an inexplicable falling off of energy. This is quite different from normal tiredness. After a good day's work, or a long walk across the fells, one may feel tired, but it's a pleasant form of exhaustion. Sitting down in a comfortable chair, the relief is most enjoyable, and one is buoyed up with a sense of achievement. All this is in complete contrast to the utter weariness experienced by the melancholic. His feeling is more like the languor following a severe illness, and for him rest offers no compensatory relief.

A depressed woman in her thirties told me that when she looked at the stairs, she wondered however she could summon the energy to climb to the top. A man, who was a regular punter, had the habit of placing a bet at the bookmaker's office on his way to work. During the early days of his depression he continued to do this, but by the evening he found himself far too exhausted to buy a paper and check the racing results. This painful weariness leads on to the next set of symptoms.

HABIT CHANGES

In a depression the daily routine, or even the habit of a lifetime may be changed. This can be quite sudden, as in the case of an old man who started to miss out the small dose of Epsom Salts he had taken each morning for many years; or the changes may be slow as shown by the proud housewife who gradually lets her standards slip. Her home becomes more and more untidy, meals are late and they are either undercooked or else burnt offerings. Her personal appearance suffers and she becomes more and more frumpish. Another example is that of the man who has the habit of dropping in at the local pub every night for a modest pint or two of ale. Sometimes he stops going out because he just cannot raise the energy to do so, and furthermore, he has been put off by his friends who keep asking him what is wrong. They have noticed that he is not himself. If he does manage to drag himself to the pub, instead of the odd pint or two, he will drink ten pints with chasers of neat whisky, as he tries vainly to find his own remedy for his problem. The avid reader gives up the habit of reading, as she cannot concentrate, or take in what she has read. Letters go unanswered and bills unpaid.

While symptoms such as these can be useful in that they draw attention to the illness, for a small minority of patients, habit changes can lead to disaster. One man started squandering his hard-earned savings on fruit machines. His wife discovered what was happening, and insisted on his coming to see me. I knew him well; he had already had a number of depressive attacks, and it was easy to persuade him to accept treatment. The gambling craze stopped abruptly. He was lucky. Thanks to the timely intervention of his wife, his extravagant spending spree was nipped in the bud. Other patients are not so fortunate.

When one woman, married with four children, developed her first depression, she became querulous, and started to quarrel violently with her husband. After one blazing row, she ran away from home and found some wretched lodgings in London. There she started to drink heavily, and after a time, discovered she had become pregnant by some stranger. She walked the Embankment contemplating suicide, but in the end she got in touch with me by telephone and I was able to persuade her to come home. She was in a state of deep depression, and from her history it was clear that the low moods had preceded the disastrous trip to London. She was fortunate in having an understanding husband who accepted that he was partly to blame for what had happened; he had known she was depressed and ill, but had failed to get medical help. She had a course of electroplexy and made a good recovery. In depression, the sexual appetite is usually lost, but sometimes, as in this case, it becomes uninhibited. As with the periodic drinker, sex becomes an attempt to find some solace in the vale of misery.

A lack of inhibition can be disastrous, for example when an elderly cleric becomes an exhibitionist. Some melancholics take to shop-lifting and end up in court. In all of these cases, the abnormal behaviour is completely out of character with the normal way of life of the individual. If the depression goes unrecognised and untreated, the unblemished reputation of a lifetime can be in ruins.

INSOMNIA

Another symptom of depression is an upset of the sleep rhythm. Once again this varies from patient to patient, but typically the melancholic has no difficulty in dropping off to sleep, but awakens in the early hours of the morning with the spirits at a very low ebb as he wonders just how to summon the energy to cope with another day of misery.

If anxiety is a prominent feature, then the victim may have difficulty in falling off to sleep. This can be blamed on the problems, real or imaginary, that keep going round and round in the patient's mind. Worry makes a restless bedfellow. Some people develop a curious form of imagery just as they begin to drop off; and this can be frightening. One man saw a series of grimacing faces that terrified him so much he became afraid to go to bed. Visions just prior to sleep are not uncommon in normal people, and those who see them regularly are not distressed. If, however, they occur for the first time in a depression, the patient puts the worst possible interpretation on the phenomena. Other melancholics are distraught by bad dreams; these nightmares can be either frightening or disgusting. The latter type only increase the sense of guilt. Sometimes the patient cannot sleep because of bodily symptoms, such as a headache, indigestion or palpitations. One woman of 54 who was deluded by the idea that she was pregnant, could not sleep because of the movements of her phantom baby. A few depressed patients sleep far too much. They tend to go to bed earlier and earlier so that they sometimes sleep the clock round, but they awaken unrefreshed, feeling far worse than when they went to bed.

There is always some change in the sleep pattern. If a depressed patient says she sleeps well, question her husband who may have a very different story. One man had to keep getting out of bed, and creeping in on the other side, his wife was so restless.

MOOD SWINGS

Another disconcerting symptom that is quite typical of a depression is the presence of mood swings. This state of affairs is most prominent at the beginning and towards the end of an episode. At this stage, the depressed person doesn't feel down all the time. The mood varies. Typically the victim feels at his worst when he awakens in the early hours, but once past midday the clouds begin to disperse, and in the evening he can feel he is back to normal, convinced after all he is going to be all right. These swings are very distressing as the hopes of the evening are dashed again and again by a renewal of the depression each morning. This symptom can keep the patient from seeing his doctor. Early in the day he feels far too ill to make the effort, and by evening he feels so well that he decides the consultation is unnecessary. This morning lethargy is so typical of a depression, it can well be the clue that leads one to the correct diagnosis.

A young married woman had consulted me over some sexual problem. During one counselling session she suddenly remarked that when she awakened in the mornings, she wondered just how she would get through the day. This symptom was characteristic of melancholia, so I started her on a course of anti-depressant drugs, and all her marital problems faded away. These mood swings are most distressing during the stage of recovery. The patient who at last realises he is on the mend can be very downcast by yet another patch of depression; he just cannot bear the idea of going through the whole horrid experience again. In some cases the rhythm is reversed. The punter mentioned earlier was able to place his bets in the morning, but by evening he felt too exhausted to check the results.

ANXIETY

Most people suffering from depression show some symptoms of anxiety. This is hardly surprising, as to find oneself suddenly removed from the comfortable normal world and into the cold cheerless realm of melancholia, demands some explanation, and the patient draws his own conclusions. The loss of drive, the sleepless nights and the increasing sense of misery, suggest to the melancholic the onset of some serious disease. Many decide it must be cancer, some a bad heart or the recrudescence of venereal disease first contracted decades ago. One patient decided he was going blind, and another for three months was convinced that she was developing poliomyelitis. When such people submit to a medical examination, it is almost invariably negative, but this offers no comfort to the patient. He feels that the disease is too subtle for the doctor to locate, or he decides the physician is just incompetent. The worst interpretation of all is that his adviser knows it's all hopeless, and is trying to cheer the patient up by deceit; it's all a big cover-up. This obsession about physical disease soon becomes an *idée fixe*, and then no number of investigations, or reassurances from doctors, relatives or friends will convince him that he is not doomed. The mind of the victim works like a scratched gramophone record, where the needle gets trapped in a groove. It goes on repeating the same dismal message over and over again. While reassurance is a waste of time, the response to adequate treatment is very different. The symptoms just disappear so that attempts to allay fears become no longer necessary.

As they sink into a depression, some patients realise that their thinking process is at fault, and so worry about mental, not physical illness. Such patients may well conclude that they are going mad. They have visions of being taken away to some mental institution, and feel that the whole family will then be denigrated by the stigma of lunacy. In fact, a depressive illness is not a form of madness. Low moods make the victim misinterpret symptoms, and misread feelings. I once played golf with a medical colleague who was depressed at the time, and actually under my care. When he had recovered he told me that he hadn't enjoyed the game a bit, because all the time he felt that the other players on the course were driving their balls straight at him. Every sound he heard appeared to him like a ball bouncing towards him. Another patient who was smoking dropped off to sleep while reading the newspaper. Somehow or other the paper caught alight and the patient awakened in horror convinced he had landed in Hades with hell fire blazing all round him.

This malfunction in thinking can be compared with a television that has gone on the blink. When the picture on the screen is distorted, it becomes a pain and a grief to watch the programme. This does not mean that the set is broken; all that is needed is some minor adjustment of the controls, and this at once restores a clear and enjoyable picture to the screen. In much the same way the melancholic's view of life can be grossly distorted, not because she is mad, but because some of the chemicals that control the brain function need to be adjusted. The cerebrum is a very sensitive organ. It is helpful to compare the depressive situation with that of the diabetic. The latter, if his sugar is badly controlled, can have blackouts and behave in a very strange way, because there is too much or too little insulin in circulation. Adjustment of the dosage soon puts things right and no one labels the diabetic as being mad in any way.

Both the fear of a deadly illness or the dread of insanity give rise to intense anxiety in the patient. She feels all on edge, jumping at any unusual sound and ready to fly off the handle at the slightest provocation. She is always expecting the worst to happen. If the telephone rings, it must be bad news; a knock on the door, and it is the police calling to say something awful has happened. Every case of severe and unexplained anxiety should be viewed as a possible problem of depression.

The symptoms are most distressing, even to an observer. The patient is restless and wide eyed, with a deadly fear written across her pallid face. She has perspiration on her brow and her hands are trembling so much that she can hardly hold a cup of tea. A psychiatrist who had suffered from a depression described his experience as a period of unspeakable agony, greyness and anxiety, the latter being far more terrifying than the simple anxieties of everyday life.

OTHER FEATURES OF DEPRESSION

There are other symptoms of this illness. The Anglo-Saxon man, with his stiff upper lip, is not supposed to cry, and as a result of this taboo, tearfulness in a British man is highly suggestive of melancholia. On the other hand, we allow women to weep in our culture, so that the tear-stained face of a woman patient is not quite so significant. Nevertheless, where there are tears, the possibility of an underlying depression should always be borne in mind.

In this illness the colour goes out of life, leaving a painful void. A Lakeland doctor, who was prone to episodes of depression, knew he was in for another bad patch when the beauty of the hills lost its appeal. He began to suffer from a distressing sense of deprivation as he gazed across a sunlit valley at a lake fringed by the vivid green of trees in the spring. While his mind told him that the scene was glorious, his heart did not respond and he felt no glow of satisfaction.

In much the same way, humour can be painful when one has completely lost the ability to laugh. The melancholic will switch off his favourite comic television programme.

Noise, especially if it is sudden, can irritate the patient, but some forms of music continue to give a measure of satisfaction. Music seems to be one distraction that does not aggravate the melancholic mood. In the Bible we read of David playing his harp, in an attempt to soothe the jangled nerves of King Saul.

The depressed person can be afflicted with many weird bodily sensations which he may find hard to describe. Conscious of a bad taste in his mouth, the patient blames his bowels which he feels have ceased to function and are indeed dead inside him. One man attributed the rumbles in his belly to the devil talking to him. Some melancholics feel that they have begun to smell and they take to hand washing and frequent changes of clothing. Such people tend to avoid company as they are so sure their smell will be noticed by others. This symptom is in fact a depressive hallucination.

When a person falls ill from a physical illness such as a heart attack, appendicitis, or some infection, the family at once rallies round and offers support to the patient. In a depressive episode, things can be very different. The symptoms don't immediately evoke sympathy, as they sound more like grumbles rather than the evidence of a genuine illness. The family can be as perplexed by his complaints as the patient himself. As a result of all this, his 'moaning' tends to be ignored, and indeed can become a source of friction. The wife feels that her husband is being awkward and difficult.

Many of the symptoms I have described tend to cut the patient off from others, so that eventually it is as if a thick piece of plate glass had been lowered between the sick person and the rest of the world. He is well aware of what is going on, but completely unable to communicate. Misunderstood by all around him and apparently unloved, he certainly has no grounds for loving himself. Life has lost all its meaning, there is no future, he is lost in black clouds of swirling misery. All this sadness is made worse by a complete lack of hope and a sense of guilt, and it is further aggravated by intense anxiety and a unique sense of loneliness.

What an agonising collection of symptoms. Every depressed person will not of necessity acquire all of them, but it doesn't take many to make life a complete misery. Once again it must be emphasised that all these morbid ideas can soon be abolished once the correct treatment has been applied.

3
The Many Moods of Melancholy

So far I have drawn a series of pictures to depict depression, in order to bring attention to an important subject that has so frequently been ignored and misunderstood. The impression may have been gained that depression is a single disease entity like appendicitis or diabetes, but this is certainly far from the truth. There are different kinds of depression and different causes of the malady. The treatment varies from case to case. The condition differs in severity, from the normal everyday type of depression that comes over all of us from time to time, to the most profound degree of all, the depressive stupor. In the latter state, the victim is unable to speak, move or sleep, but remains acutely aware of his surroundings in an abysm of utter misery, a prisoner of his own mind, bound to the ruthless rack of melancholia. The complex problem of the depressive disorders demands some clarification.

NORMAL EVERYDAY DEPRESSION

Depression of this kind is a universal experience. I feel depressed when my wife tells me she has crashed the car. I feel even more depressed if I do the same thing myself, as then the condition is aggravated by a sense of guilt. Why was I so careless or so stupid?

All sorts of mundane events put us in low spirits. The housewife feels pretty wretched when on Monday morning she finds that the washing machine won't work, and no mechanic will be available for a week. Life is full of such situations that give rise to a transient sense of depression. Given time we either work out a solution or come to terms with the problem; we usually find ways and means of dealing with 'the slings and arrows of outrageous fortune'.

Some people are, however, bowled over by the stress and strain of the situation, so that the low moods assume the proportions of an illness, and this we call a reactive depression.

REACTIVE DEPRESSION

If the adverse circumstances are too severe, or one calamity follows another, or if the stressful situation lasts too long, the victim may well develop symptoms of a pathological depression. Women are more likely to fall victim to this state than men. The patient becomes tearful, irritable and on edge. Sleepless nights sap her failing energy even more, so that she becomes unable to live the normal life to which she was accustomed. The treatment consists of listening to the patient's story, supplemented by some form of counselling. Details of these measures will be described in Chapter 5.

ENDOGENOUS DEPRESSION

The literal meaning of this term is that it is a form of melancholia that comes from within and is not related to outside circumstances. It is not as common as reactive depression, and it has certain distinctive features. Men are just as likely to contract this illness as women. There seems to be a genetic link, as the condition tends to run in certain families. I knew one family in which four brothers were affected out of six. Attacks come on suddenly, out of the blue, and often episodes are liable to recur all through life. This illness responds well to physical forms of treatment, such as drugs, or (more rarely used) an electric treatment called electroplexy or electro-convulsive therapy (ECT). There are drugs today that can actually prevent attacks from recurring. Some of these patients suffer from a phasic illness called manic-depressive disease. This means that the stage of depression can be ushered in or followed by a period of elation called mania.

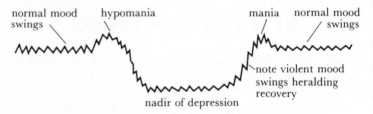

normal mood swings hypomania mania normal mood swings

note violent mood swings heralding recovery

nadir of depression

The course of an endogenous depression.

Mania

Like depression, this illness varies in intensity. It is the complete opposite of depression. In the early stages of elation, the victim feels extremely fit and well; clear-headed, ambitious, full of energy and capable of doing immense amounts of work. He never seems to tire, can survive on a very small amount of sleep, and cannot stop talking. People who have had this mild form of mania thoroughly enjoy the experience. They assert that never to have passed through such a phase is never to have lived, it is so productive and enjoyable. The patient carries with him an aura of jollity, so that for a time any audience enjoys his company and his jokes. The patient can become quite a wit.

A woman recovering from a depressive episode ran into a bout of mild mania. She had boundless energy and could not stop working. Her husband, alarmed at her activities, urged her to relax, and go a bit slower. She told him she could no

24

more sit down and take things easy than a child with measles could wipe away his spots! When I asked her how she was, she told me she was still meeting herself coming back!

In moderation this mood is acceptable, but if it becomes severe it is then unpleasant for all concerned. The victim's sense of judgement goes, so that his good ideas become spurious and absurd. One man was convinced that he had perfected a system of betting and was sure he could make a fortune which he intended to spend on all sorts of charity. A manic cleric who felt he was called by God to convert prostitutes from their evil ways, landed himself in a lot of compromising situations. Money is lavishly spent; there is a demand for parties at which the victim holds forth all the time, and his talking is punctuated by blue or completely inappropriate jokes. The manic person gets physically exhausted from all his activities, but is completely unable to let up, and sleep becomes impossible. He becomes irritable, and if crossed in any way, can become violent.

From the very start, the manic person cannot see that he is ill, and any form of treatment or restraint is rejected out of hand. The most severe forms of mania are in fact far from pleasant for the patient. I have known such patients burst into tears as the tension inside them becomes unbearable; and some who have recovered have pleaded with me not to let them get excited again.

If it is bad for the patient, for the family it is a calamity. Relatives are constantly frightened, embarrassed or completely humiliated by the situation. A woman who was the wife of a doctor liable to these violent mood swings, told me that she could cope with her husband when he was depressed but in the stage of elation he became quite impossible. Mania is much more common among people of Afro-Caribbean descent and only occurs in some four per cent of white races. Like depression, it responds to modern drug treatment.

A married woman with four children called to see my

partner with a weight problem. He told me after the surgery that he had thoroughly enjoyed the consultation, she was so vivacious and interesting. She had talked about classical music, and he had been amazed at her knowledge. Neither he nor I thought of it at the time, but what had made her so interesting was a mild state of mania, and it was the infectious nature of her elation that had made her so entertaining. At that time she had taken to dancing, and she frequently went out with her husband, and they waltzed together until the early hours of the morning. She found she had boundless energy and life was just wonderful.

After a few weeks she started an inexorable slide downhill into depression, and then, try as she might, found it impossible to keep up the pace. She discovered that a few drinks helped to boost her morale, but she started to quarrel with her husband. In the end she went off to London, and the outcome of that has already been described in Chapter 2, 'Habit Changes'.

If only we doctors had spotted the elation as a symptom of mania, we could have saved her from a series of disasters. Perhaps we can be excused for failing to spot the symptom, as it was her first attack. With people who are prone to manic-depressive illness, unusual high spirits are soon recognised as a prelude to depression, and appropriate action can then be taken.

Disguised Forms of Endogenous Depression

More than any other illness, endogenous depression can closely imitate other forms of disease, so that the sick person appears to be suffering from anxiety, a physical illness, or even schizophrenia.

A middle-aged woman came to see me asking for a tonic as she felt run down. A complete examination found no evidence of any physical disease, but she was certainly a very anxious type of person. I spent some time getting her to talk. In the end she admitted that she was very worried because her younger son was about to marry an undesirable girl, of whom she did not approve. I knew both families well, and it was soon clear to me that her story of the bad marriage was just a way to explain her misery. The bride was a fine girl, and the marriage over the years has proved to be a great success. The spurious worry was in fact the start of a menopausal endogenous depression. Anxiety is often the first symptom of a depression and it can appear before any feelings of dejection.

One woman first came to see me worried about her throat. I could find no evidence of any disease, nor could the specialist to whom she was referred. Reassurance gave her no satisfaction, but after a few months she recovered. A few years later she came back to see me complaining of pains in her pelvis, and once again neither the specialist nor I could find any organic lesion, and after a few months, she had made a complete recovery. When the same thing happened for the third time, the penny dropped. Her periodic attacks of anxiety were in fact episodes of endogenous depression, but she never sank into a state of melancholia. Once the diagnosis had been made, the treatment was easy. Antidepressant drugs rapidly removed the symptoms, and what is more, she came to recognise when she needed treatment. Irrational periodic anxiety can well be a mild endogenous depression, the patient not having reached the threshold of depression.

A youth of 23 came to see me with a woolly cap pulled well down over his ears. He complained that he was going prematurely bald. Indeed, when I looked at him, his hair was receding at the temples, but it hadn't detracted from his good looks. To him it was a calamity, it had made him utterly miserable, and he told me it had blighted his life. He was ashamed to take off his hat; he had broken with his girlfriend, and although he managed to hold his job, he had

stopped going out to enjoy social activities. Further questioning showed that he had just passed through a period of
intense activity. He had inherited a house from his grandfather, and he had set about transforming the garden. He
had literally moved many tons of soil in landscaping the plot
and all this was on top of a hard day's work in the local
brickyard. The original complaint of losing his hair was no
illusion, but the real illness lay not in his scalp, but deep in
the mind beneath it. The problem looked like endogenous
depression, and this theory was supported by the period of
productive elation. After a course of anti-depressant drugs,
he ceased to worry about his hair. Three years later he had a
second attack. This time his scalp no longer worried him; he
was fearful in case he was getting cancer. This dread cleared
after a further course of treatment.

The mimicry of organic disease can be very deceptive. A
woman of 57 came to see me complaining of constipation.
When I examined her, I found her abdomen so grossly
distended with wind, I referred her as an emergency to the
local hospital. The surgeon agreed that there was a blockage
in the bowels, and he operated to look for the cause of her
trouble. No physical obstruction was found, the wound was
closed, and a few days later she returned home. I then
uncovered symptoms of a depression, and furthermore, I
found previous episodes of the illness. In this instance, the
melancholia had caused an upset of the nerves which control
the tone of the bowel muscles. As a result there had been a
general relaxation of the gut walls and bowel distension had
followed. Physical treatment for her depression cleared up
her troubles. However, the presenting symptoms of bowel
trouble had deceived a whole series of doctors.

Pain is a very common symptom of depression. In a survey
on the subject I found that some 35 per cent of depressed
patients, when first seen, complained of pain in some form.
One man came to the surgery with extremely tender testicles. This was a great embarrassment to him, as people

kept asking him why he was limping. It was indeed difficult to walk, and he had to take the greatest care when he sat down. I could find no abnormality in his testicles, nor could the specialist to whom he was referred. The pains got worse and he was constantly in tears. Pain-killing tablets had no effect, but once he had embarked on a course of anti-depressant drugs, the pain disappeared. Any inexplicable pain, like some forms of faceache that puzzle both doctor and dentist, can be an expression of this type of melancholia.

Depression is certainly the great imitator. Overleaf is a list showing the very first symptom complained of by the patient, in an illness which was shown in time to stem from a depressive syndrome.

A young woman of 25 came to see me one morning complaining that people were talking about her. She felt that the girls at the office were laughing at her, and implying by their sniggers that she was pregnant. As she sat in my room, she cocked her head to listen to the voices. I was so worried about her, I took her home and questioned her parents. They told me that she had been acting in a strange way for only a few days, but they confirmed my fears that she was developing schizophrenia, which is the most unpleasant form of mental illness. I put her to bed and gave her large doses of the appropriate medicament. In a week all her symptoms had gone. I lowered the dosage but kept up the treatment for some three months, and at a follow up some twenty years later, I found her fit and well, and over all that time she had had no further trouble.

Endogenous depression can imitate any known disease, and this includes schizophrenia. Schizophrenia tends to be progressive and leaves permanent damage, whereas endogenous depression is a periodic illness, from which the patient makes a complete recovery. Over the years I found that a number of patients with a schizophrenic-like illness made a good recovery. These were in fact probably all cases of endogenous depression in disguise. One woman who had

Presenting Symptoms in Manic-Depressive Disease

	Presenting Symptom	Number of Cases		Presenting Symptom	Number of Cases
1	Tired, short of energy, feels weak or run down	135	36	Anorexia	3
2	Headache	70	37	Impotence	3
3	Feelings of anxiety or tension	42	38	Sore tongue or mouth	3
4	Depression	27	39	Catarrh	3
5	Backache	25	40	Pains in genitalia	2
6	Insomnia	22	41	Amenorrhoea	2
7	Pains in chest	20	42	Bad taste	2
8	Dyspepsia	18	43	Failing memory	2
9	Giddiness	17	44	Fear of mental illness	2
10	Pains in trunk, arms, or legs	13	45	Restless feelings	2
11	Cough	10	46	Cold	2
12	Globus syndrome	10	47	Earache	2
13	Abdominal pain	8	48	Fugue	1
14	Faints, fits, bouts	8	49	Blinking	1
15	Tinnitus	7	50	Pseudocyesis	1
16	Hot flushes	7	51	Dysmenorrhoea	1
17	Neuralgia	7	52	Heavy losses	1
18	Irritability	6	53	Fear of pregnancy	1
19	Trembling feelings	6	54	Wants to break engagement	1
20	Palpitations	6	55	Trouble with children	1
21	Keeps crying	6	56	Bleeding gums	1
22	Dyspnoea	6	57	Fear of responsibility	1
23	Pains in neck	6	58	Fear of dying	1
24	Pruritus	6	59	Fear of venereal disease	1
25	Feelings of unreality	5	60	Loss of hair	1
26	Diarrhoea	5	61	Varicose veins	1
27	Defective vision	5	62	Blushing	1
28	Skin rash	4	63	Increase in weight	1
29	Fear of cancer	4	64	Morning misery	1
30	Panic attacks	4	65	Ideas of reference	1
31	Loss of interest in things	4	66	Bad dreams	1
32	Loss of weight	4	67	Fear of being alone	1
33	Hypersomnia	4	68	Fear of lump in abdomen	1
34	Sickly feelings	3	69	Fear of poverty	1
35	Irregular menses	3	70	Fear of heart disease	1
			71	Acute grief	1

Reproduced with kind permission of John Wright (publishers), Bristol.

suffered from schizophrenic episodes for over forty years, has been free from attacks now for fifteen years since she was given a special form of treatment for depression. Periodic illnesses of any kind are strongly suggestive of depression. While endogenous depression is liable to recur, some victims just have a single attack. The young woman with the schizophrenic-like illness was such a case.

ENDOGENOUS-LIKE DEPRESSION

This is rather a cumbersome term but it covers a large proportion of depressed people, some of whom are seriously ill. I have suggested that cases of reactive depression should be treated by counselling, but unfortunately not all respond favourably. The basic cause of the misery may not be in doubt, but in spite of every effort to support the patient and explain her troubles, she cannot throw off her despondent moods, or she starts to live in a world of fantasy. Many of this type of case have what I call 'an endogenous feel', about them, and respond well to anti-depressant drugs.

A middle-aged woman came to see me because she felt run down and wretched. I had no difficulty in getting her to talk, and it was soon clear that the trouble was tied up in her domestic situation. She had suffered from a series of distressing events. She felt miserable because her son and his family had emigrated to Australia, and she missed them terribly. A week before, the dog they had had for ten years had been killed by a car in the street. Finally she was upset about her husband's uncaring attitude. He was a lorry driver, and the job meant that he spent many nights away from home. After listening to this tale of woe, I felt that I must see the husband; it was important to hear what he had to say, and she agreed to bring him along to the next interview. I liked the man, and he was obviously most concerned about his wife's state. While he sympathised with her complaint about his work, he pointed out that the awkward hours were just part of his job, for which he was well paid. He didn't feel he could afford to change his occupation. He then asked a very pertinent question. Why was his wife finding the routine so intolerable, when she had accepted it ever since he had taken on the job after his demobilisation from the army? He went on to say that he had never known her so miserable and querulous; she was certainly not herself. His observations made me realise that while the depression had been precipitated by a whole series of adverse events, the case had endogenous features. I tried her on anti-depressant drugs, she improved, and after a few weeks she was wondering why she had made such a fuss about things.

The wife of a man who ran a small business was kept occupied running the home and caring for her children. Her husband had a heart attack and was rushed into hospital and it was several weeks before he recovered. Somehow or other the wife managed to cope, taking on the running of the shop as well as all her own work. When her husband was well again they went back to the old routine. Then he had a second and fatal attack. This time the shock was too much for her; she started telling her friends that he wasn't dead, but had gone away on holiday. She was so disturbed she needed hospital care and attention. After a few weeks she recovered, came home, and with the help of some good friends was able to run both the shop and her home. She never had a relapse.

This patient's depression was certainly reactive, caused by the loss of her husband, but it had many features of an endogenous depression, and she responded rapidly and well to drug treatment. A number of people with reactive depression are reduced to a very low state by all their misfortunes, and features of an endogenous state emerge. The treatment required is a combination of support and drug therapy, or, in a few cases, electroplexy.

SYMPTOMATIC DEPRESSION

As I have already stated, the brain is a very sensitive organ, and it can be upset by major variations in its basic needs. It can also be made to malfunction by a whole host of toxic agents.

Our bodies are under the influence of chemicals called hormones, which are rather more complex in women than in men. They are produced by glands such as the ovaries and testicles; the thyroid in the neck; the adrenals above the kidneys; and the pituitary lying just below the brain.

Women are more sensitive to hormone fluctuations than men, because there is a regular switching from one agent to another, which is the basis of the menstrual cycle. Some women are upset by the blend of their hormones just before they have a period, which can give rise to quite a severe mini-depression every month. For two or three days they become scratchy and miserable. There are a number of ways in which pre-menstrual tension can be treated, and those who suffer from it should certainly consult their doctors about it.

After the birth of a baby there is a further drastic change in hormone levels, but the stresses and strains which follow this event will be dealt with later in the book.

Sometimes people get in a low state because the body is short of some vital substance. For example, if the thyroid gland ceases to function adequately, retardation and frank depression may follow, which as a rule clears when thyroid tablets are prescribed. Occasionally the patient seems to have been so conditioned by his low state that anti-depressant drugs are also needed.

Shortage of the various forms of Vitamin B can cause this trouble, particularly in the third world, where dietetic deficiencies are rampant. In black South African communities, diseases such as pellagra and beriberi, both caused by a shortage of the Vitamin B complex, often present with symptoms of depression. Many people admitted to South African mental hospitals were found to be suffering from these diseases.

The famous explorer and navigator, Captain James Cook, showed that by giving his sailors fresh fruit and vegetables, scurvy could be eliminated from his crew. Up to that time, the ship's company on long voyages could be decimated by the disease, which we now know was due to a lack of Vitamin C in the diet. James Watt, a naval historian, in *The Medical Problems of the Voyages of two Northern Circumnavigators* (Newcastle University, 1985), has suggested that on Cook's last voyage, he fell victim to a deficiency of Vitamin B. He became morose and ill, and because of this, lost his skill in the handling of both his crew and the natives of the islands which he visited, although he had always been noted for his ability in man-management. Watt suggested that this loss of finesse caused his death at the hands of the islanders in Hawaii. If this theory is true, it is paradoxical that the man who discovered the cure for one form of vitamin deficiency should die from the shortage of another.

The only people in Britain likely to suffer shortages in Vitamin B are the aged, some of whom tend to live on convenience foods rather than a good mixed diet. When the level of Vitamin B12 drops too low, this causes anaemia, but the onset can be very insidious, and depression can precede the anaemia by months or even years. A medical colleague became very worried as she was sure she had a bowel cancer. Full investigation failed to show up any such problem, but as both her father and grandfather had died of anaemia, great attention was paid to her blood – there was no evidence that she had inherited the family complaint. She became so low and miserable that she was referred to a psychiatrist. He very wisely suggested that the standard treatment for anaemia at the time, which consisted of injections of a concentrated liver extract, while it might do no good, could certainly do no harm. She was given this treatment and within days she had recovered her good spiritis and the bowel symptoms vanished. Her depression, which had a typical endogenous appearance, was in fact due to a deficiency of Vitamin B12. This delay in diagnosis could not happen today, because the blood level of this vitamin can now be measured accurately, long before there is a sign of any anaemia.

There are a number of toxic agents that give rise to depression. The most common of these is some factor derived from a virus infection. Those that cause influenza and glandular fever are the most common culprits, but any virus or indeed any infection can leave an aftermath of melancholia. I attended an old man of 70 who was down in the dumps following influenza; he was making very heavy weather of his recovery. One evening I noticed in the local newspaper that he had been left a legacy. I was sure that this would cheer him up, but when I saw him, the windfall had not made the slightest difference; he was still as miserable as ever. It was several more weeks before the depression cleared and he was able to enjoy his new-found wealth. Today, this problem would be treated with anti-depressant drugs.

Sometimes the misery is the result of an allergy. Sensitivity to the vast array of modern drugs is not uncommon and, although food allergies are rare among adults, they are more frequent among children. Some women are upset by the contraceptive pill. One woman described her wretchedness by saying she felt like a 'caponised chicken'. The answer to this particular problem is to find an alternative form of contraceptive. Drugs prescribed by the doctor can cause depression in susceptible people. A man I was treating for blood pressure became retarded and depressed and I suspected that this was due to the drug he was taking. Even when I stopped the tablets, it was some time before he recovered. Proof that they were to blame was clearly shown by an unfortunate mistake. When I was on holiday, the locum gave him a further supply of the same drug, and within hours he had sunk back into a deep depression, and slowly recovered again once the tablets were stopped.

Most depressions caused by a toxic agent such as a virus, last for a long time after the removal of the causal agent. This is very different from the melancholia brought about by a deficiency. By and large, once the missing substance is replaced, a rapid improvement is soon noticed.

One of the most common chemical agents to cause depression is alcohol. Addicts to this drug are very liable to bouts of misery and remorse, especially when, at last, they realise that they have become victims of a pernicious habit they seem powerless to break; a habit that is threatening their family life, and perhaps their jobs. Alcoholics are not popular employees. This book is not the place to describe the treatment of alcoholism. Briefly the patient needs specialist counselling and probably some institutional care. Antidepressant drugs are not an answer to this problem.

There is another link between alcoholism and depression. Melancholia can literally drive a man to drink. An army sergeant was admitted to my care, suffering from delirium tremens. He was vividly hallucinating with horrible visions of snakes. He had lost a lot of weight and had 'the shakes', and was generally in poor shape. Large doses of the Vitamin B complex soon restored him, and when he had recovered he had an interesting story to relate. He had grown very morose and depressed and had suffered from many typical depressive symptoms. He found that a heavy dose of brandy helped him to sleep, and before long he discovered that a few drams on waking seemed to dispel the hangover. It wasn't long before he was depending more on brandy than food to keep him going. Before this depression he had never touched alcohol, and this was confirmed by his wife. By the time I saw him, a remission from the depression had already set in, and once he had recovered his appetite and abandoned the brandy bottle, he had virtually recovered. His drinking had been a symptom, not a cause, of endogenous depression.

Some melancholics behave like this from time to time, with months of sobriety between bouts of drinking. It is the periodicity of the attacks that gives the clue to the correct diagnosis. Teetotallers or social drinkers who from time to time drink themselves silly for a few weeks or months are likely to be suffering from endogenous depression. Treatment with anti-depressant drugs or even electroplexy can in these cases cut short the episode of drinking.

Head injuries can cause depression, and the condition may take a long time to clear. A butcher was delivering his meat on a foggy day when he was knocked down and rendered unconscious. He lost all his drive, had sleep problems and became thoroughly miserable. A large sum of money in compensation made no difference to his condition. Serious injuries of any kind can give rise to an aftermath of depression. One of the sisters in the local cottage hospital sustained a nasty fracture of her thigh bone which meant rest in bed for many weeks. She became very low spirited, but this was noted by the orthopaedic surgeon who prescribed anti-depressant drugs. This upset the nurse even more. She had always felt that anyone needing to take 'nerve tablets' must be feeble, and she resented this implication applied to herself. She was, however, wise enough to obey orders, and when I saw her ten days later she was very much better. She asked me how it was that a few tablets could change so dramatically the way one felt.

It has long been known that people living in remote communities in such places as Scandinavia or Switzerland, cut off from the rest of the world by heavy snowfalls, are prone to depressive illness towards the end of the long winter. This was in part due simply to the plain monotony of life, because with the advent of radio and television, the disease is not so common as it was. On the other hand, it has recently been shown that some individuals are sensitive to deprivation from sunlight, which might well be a contributory factor to the depression. With cases of this nature, the low moods are quickly abolished by exposure to ultra-violet light.

CHRONIC DEPRESSION

Unfortunately there are a few depressed people who fail to respond to all forms of orthodox medical treatment. They are a real problem to themselves, their families and to their doctors. The treatment of such cases is complicated and long term. A description of how to deal with this problem is dealt with at length in Chapter 7.

The discovery of anti-depressant drugs was a great medical advance, but it must be emphasised that these agents are not a cure-all for every kind of depression. The drugs for each patient have to be selected with great attention and, as with all treatments for any disease, sympathy and understanding bound up in what amounts to 'tender loving care' are important ingredients.

4
No Age Immune

INFANCY

Depression can afflict people of all ages, even very small babies. When I was a medical student, there was often the odd case of what was called 'pink disease' in the children's ward. These little lobster-coloured infants were a picture of misery, unable to sleep, constantly crying as they writhed about in their cots, and they took several weeks to recover. It was later discovered that the illness was due to mercury poisoning. It was indeed the custom to add a small dose of calomel to teething powders, which had been a popular across-the-counter remedy. Mercury has long since been banned from teething powders, and indeed, teething powders themselves have gone. We no longer see pink disease. In infancy depression is a rare malady. Probably the commonest cause of it today is child abuse.

Older children can suffer from severe endogenous depression. Reactive states are not uncommon. The moods of children are specially volatile. Normal everyday depressions are commonplace among children of all ages, as quarrels are inevitable. Some juveniles sink into reactive states due to unhappiness in the home or at school. Endogenous depression is rare, but it does occur. My attention was drawn to it by the following case.

A young woman of 19 was engaged to be married when suddenly, for no adequate reason, she decided to call off the wedding. Her parents could not understand her attitude, and she was persuaded to come and see me. I knew her well and it was easy to get her to talk. She could find no logical reason for her change of heart; she still loved her fiancé, but felt in some way unworthy of his affection. The overall picture was one of endogenous depression. In those days the only active treatment was electroplexy which meant admission to the local mental hospital; no easy choice for the young woman. However, she accepted my advice, had the treatment and made a good recovery. She married her boyfriend and their life together was a very happy one, in spite of the fact that over the years she has had a number of recurrent depressive attacks. Her mother told me that the girl had been much the same when she was ten, and went on to point out that I had attended her! I looked up my notes and found that for a number of weeks she had suffered from school refusal, inability to sleep, and she was constantly in tears. These details convinced me that this must have been her first attack of endogenous depression, an episode I had failed to recognise.

A few months later I picked up a similar case of a girl who had just passed her eleven-plus examination to go to grammar school, and her mother told me she had had much the same reaction as the other case when she was 6. It is now accepted that about one child in every thousand seems to be afflicted in this way. The main symptoms are misery, loss of self-esteem, problems with sleeping and eating, bedwetting and school refusal. The most convincing diagnostic evidence is that, for a period, the child adopts a behaviour pattern quite different from the usual routine. An observant teacher may well spot such a child, as there is a falling-off of the standard of work, and the victim may lose all his friends, and so become isolated from the group. These endogenous attacks are easy to overlook, which is a pity as children can respond to drug treatment.

Small children are particularly sensitive to allergies, which can give rise to asthma, skin rashes, behaviour problems, and the depressive syndromes. Over-activity is one feature of this trouble, when the child behaves like a person with mania, and as such can be a real problem to his parents. Food preservatives and colouring agents can sometimes be the cause of the ceaseless movements. Once this has been spotted and removed, the child rapidly returns to normal behaviour, but a single dose of the offending substance can make him hyperactive again in a matter of minutes. Medical advice should be sought for problems of this kind.

ADOLESCENCE

With the advent of adolescence, the young person tends to be pulled in two directions, and this can produce a very stressful situation. While he appreciates the love, attention, and especially the approval of his parents, the desire for independence is also there; he wants to become a person in his own right. This may be a laudable objective, but it often causes friction as it implies finding different company, sometimes with a different lifestyle, clothes, fashions, and eating habits. During this phase of life the emotions are still volatile, and the young person is easily upset, resents criticism and may be very hurtful towards his parents when he speaks his mind. At the same time he longs to retain the old sense of security derived from parental support and affection. In this highly-charged atmosphere, it is not surprising to find that there is a considerable increase in the number of depressive reactions. Unfortunately at no stage in life are they more difficult to locate and treat. The desire for independence tends to prevent the young person from discussing his problems with the older generation, who are regarded as being too orthodox and set in their ways. The young person thinks he knows the kind of answer he will get to any questions, so why waste time asking them? He may well discuss matters with his contemporaries, or he may prefer to battle on his own. As in time most reactive depressions are resolved, and with the endogenous type the illness is self-limiting, and in the end fades away, most of the young folk who suffer from depressive episodes emerge safely through the storms of adolescence. They are certainly helped through this awkward period by the kindly tolerance of loving parents, guidance from wise teachers, and the support of religion if they are church members. Those who run youth clubs can do much to help these young people. If those responsible for young people can spot a case of endogenous depression, the victim can be expected to respond well to treatment, if he can be persuaded to take it. The youth described in Chapter 2 (page 12), who felt such a step was a waste of time, is a good example of what can happen.

Something like ten per cent of pupils go on from schools to become students at universities, polytechnics and teachers' training institutions. This highly talented group are very prone to bouts of depression; more so than their contemporaries who have remained at home and found remunerative employment. Many freshers uprooted from familiar territory and the home background suffer badly from homesickness. Some feel vaguely jealous of their age group who are already earning good money in the congenial environment of their home town. With the inevitable financial problems of the student, they wonder if they have been wise to choose an academic career. How to manage on their allowance is a constant worry. The atmosphere of the college is completely foreign to some of them, and they may have difficulty in getting on with fellow students, especially those of the opposite sex. On the other hand, the *milieu* provides so many counter-attractions by way of sport, the arts, and debate, that too much time may be spent on such activities, and the student may do badly in examinations. The stress of this situation gets worse as finals approach, and to this is added the worry of whether or not the young person will find a job once he has qualified, as academic ability carries no guarantee of employment. All these stresses bring a quota of depressive illnesses, and while the majority of students learn to cope with the situation, some break down with over-whelming reactive depressions, and there are always a few who will succumb to the endogenous variety. Fortunately most universities and colleges are geared to take care of their students with tutors who take a special interest in each individual and a health service trained to deal with any specific problems. Furthermore, young people themselves are more willing to talk about their worries than they were in the previous stage of adolescence. If he is wise enough to seek it, the depressed student has a very good chance of getting all the help he needs.

PREGNANCY AND CHILDBIRTH

During pregnancy and after childbirth there are quite violent changes in the hormone levels. The first three months after conception may be quite a trial as the mother feels somehow different and at times really uncomfortable. She tends to tire easily, which may make her irritable. She may resent sexual approaches from her husband. Morning sickness is unpleasant and puts her off her food, while the pressure of her growing womb may make her need to pass water frequently and upset her sleep.

However, once past the first three months, most women's spirits rise and they can pass through a stage of elation, never having felt so well in their lives. During the final six months, depression is a rare event. The mother certainly feels tired again towards the end of pregnancy as the sheer weight of all she has to carry becomes a burden, but any inconvenience is far outweighed by a joyful sense of anticipation.

Once the baby has arrived there are again striking changes in the hormones. These act to produce milk in the breasts, and to make the huge empty womb shrink back to its normal size. Once the baby is safely born, the mother can experience a sense of exhilaration. She has accomplished a very hard and difficult task, which gives her a deep sense of achievement. After months of waiting, she is thrilled to have the baby in her arms, and she is deeply satisfied by the loving congratulations of her husband. All she has worked for for over nine months has at last come about. However, such a sense of elation doesn't last. A few days later she may pass through a phase of disappointment and become disillusioned. The baby cries, the mother's tail is sore, and her enlarged breasts throb. Chemical changes in the blood combined with environmental upsets tend to give rise to a transient depression known as the 'four day blues'. It is small wonder she feels tearful and despondent. After a few days this mood passes, and the mother settles down to the new way of life with her baby.

With perhaps one in ten of mothers, a second type of depression occurs. A sense of lethargy sets in a few weeks after the birth and a few never really recover from the 'four day blues'. The woman feels short of energy and generally 'under the weather'. It is certainly not uncommon for a young mother to say that she has never felt really well since the birth of her baby. It is important that such people should seek treatment, both for their own sake and for that of the baby. A despondent mother lacks the maternal warmth that is so vital to the needs of the new-born during the first few weeks of life. The treatment of such cases begins with supportive counselling, but anti-depressant drugs are often needed. One such patient was telling me all about her worries, when she revealed that the worst part of her day was when she awakened in the early hours of the morning and started to brood over her troubles. She told me that prior to the birth, she had never had any problems with her sleep. This upset in her sleep rhythm was so typical of endogenous depression, she was given a course of the appropriate drugs and she soon returned to normal. It has been suggested that this syndrome may be due to a deficiency of a trace element, zinc, and small doses of this metal can rectify this situation.

It is most important for both husband and wife to spot and report this form of melancholia, the onset of which can be insidious, and if untreated, low moods and vague ill health can persist for a very long time.

There is a third type of post-natal depression which is both severe and alarming. Fortunately it is a rare disease. It comes on a few days or weeks after the birth, and the patient is so disturbed that the diagnosis is never in doubt. As a rule the sick woman needs to be cared for in a psychiatric hospital for a while. This is a thoroughly distressing event for all concerned but happily the outlook is very good. No matter how bad the patient seems at the time, recovery is the general rule.

THE CHANGE OF LIFE

Most animals can go on having offspring to the end of their lives. With human beings, things are different; at around fifty a woman ceases to have her monthly periods and this climacteric is known as the change of life, or the menopause. Once again there are considerable changes in hormone levels, and these can cause hot flushes and many other unpleasant symptoms. Mental depression is so common at this age that a special term has been coined for it, namely involutional melancholia. This illness is not entirely due to hormonal changes. Juggling with a variety of ovarian extracts may relieve some symptoms, but once a depression has set in, it is rarely cleared by hormonal treatment. At this time a woman is confronted by a number of problems. The cessation of her periods may be welcomed as freedom from the 'curse', and from the danger of an unwanted pregnancy, but at the same time it spells the end of reproductive life. In a sense the woman has been neutered, and in the deep recesses of her mind she resents this, she is no longer a whole woman. The end of reproductive life does not mean that sexual relationships inevitably finish; indeed freedom from the need to use any form of contraception can increase the pleasure of the act.

At this time, the children have left home or are about to do so. A woman may recognise that this is indeed the way of life, and she may be glad for their sake that they have gained their independence, but part of her resents the change. It can be a big wrench to her maternal feelings. Unless she can find other interests, life tends to seem futile and empty. She may even feel jealous of her husband, who at this age is at the peak of his performance, and perhaps more interested in his work than home. It is the blend of hormonal upsets and social circumstances that tends to make depression more common at the menopause than at any other time in a woman's life. Happily the condition responds well to treatment.

Men too have a climacteric. It comes a good deal later in life, is more gradual, and is not so prone to produce a depressive reaction.

BEREAVEMENT

One universal form of depression is that which follows a bereavement. This can be quite devastating, especially when it occurs unexpectedly, or if it is a young person who has died. In some ways modern medicine, with all its expectation of miracle cures has made mourning more difficult than it was fifty years ago. Today, if parents lose a young child, they are very much on their own, it is such a rare event. In the past, children died from diphtheria and scarlet fever; adolescents faded away once they had contracted pulmonary tuberculosis. Few weeks would pass without the vision of a funeral procession making its way to the church with the parents carrying the small coffin. As the cortège passed by, people on the footpath stood still, and the menfolk removed their headgear as a token of respect. Every street had parents

46

who had traversed through the same vale of misery, and there was a whole set of customs, a recognised ritual, to be observed. The mourners all wore black, or if they could not afford it, black armbands, and the wealthy had special stationery printed with a black edge to the paper and envelopes. The funeral was always followed by a wake at which relatives and friends assembled for a meal; they cried together and sometimes laughed together as they remembered incidents in the life of the departed. All these customs went a long way towards alleviating the devastation.

Today, because early death is not so common, many of these formalities have been forgotten and abandoned. Friends can be at a loss to know what to say or do. A young man lost his fiancée in a road accident. His friends didn't like to talk about it, in case they upset him, and for the same reason he was not invited to join their parties. He was in fact deserted and isolated when he most needed help. No harm is ever done by talking sympathetically to a bereaved person. To ignore them can be hurtful. It is important to keep up social contacts in the weeks and months following the loss, for to be really effective the support must be continuous.

Death is certainly a sad event, but it is natural and something that is bound to happen to all of us. Time is the great healer, and with the support of family and friends, most people adjust to the situation. Advanced planning can go far to ease the distress. One couple had made a point of discussing in great detail what should happen when one of them died. The wife was a very dependent person, and when her husband died first, I wondered how she would cope. However, they had planned that the survivor should move into an Abbeyfield House, which is a form of sheltered accommodation. This is what she did, and she settled in well knowing that she was carrying out the wishes of her husband.

As a rough rule, a man should be able to go back to work two weeks after the event; but a complete recovery takes much more time. Until the first year has passed, life is full of painful anniversaries. It is most important to keep active and the man with a job is lucky to have this distraction. A widow, especially if she has been well provided for, is likely to find time weighing heavily on her hands. She should find some part-time employment or undertake voluntary work. All sorts of novel ideas have proved very useful; one woman went off to London and had a crash course on how to play bridge. She then joined the local club of which she is now a popular member. Another widow, who had a sleep problem, used to lie in bed going over all the most exciting holidays she had had with her husband. This gave her considerable pleasure until sleep took over. Torrie's little book, *Begin Again* (Dent, London, 1970), is full of good advice for those who mourn, and the Cruse organisation that she founded can provide useful support and much needed friendship. (For further details of this organisation, *see* Chapter 7.) Sometimes the state of depression is such that medical help is needed.

RETIREMENT

Married women who have not been out at work don't retire in the same way as their husbands. They carry on their household chores. If a retired man is willing to collaborate, the housewife is able to take things a bit easier by delegating some of the work. Men don't have a bodily climacteric like the female menopause, but retirement is certainly a comparable event, and as such it is a period when men are prone to depression. The adverse effects of this enormous change lie in the loss of a routine way of life, the loss of good fellowship with work-mates, and for some, a loss of status. The business tycoon can become a nobody overnight. There is inevitably a drop in the family income to add to his worries. It isn't easy to contemplate adjusting to a lower standard of living, and some may even feel caught in a poverty trap, although they have to admit they are far more affluent than were their parents and grandparents. There are certain compensations which mitigate the situation. Several concessions can be available, such as cheap travel, and lower prices at the theatre and cinema. Holidays can be taken at off-peak periods, often at a very reasonable price. The organisation SAGA Holidays Ltd (at 119 Stangate Road, Folkestone, Kent) is geared to provide all kinds of holiday facilities for pensioners. Women may well share the anxieties about finance, but if they have not been working they don't have the sudden cut-off from their daily routine, and this could well be a factor that has tended to allow them to live longer than men.

Husband and wife being together all day long can make for difficulties. The woman may find it difficult to modify a routine to which she has grown accustomed, and may well resent her husband under her feet all day long, especially if he does not lend a hand with some of the household tasks, or if he is given to grumbling about having nothing to do. The pair tend to run short of small talk. This is one phase in life when depression derived from uprooting and boredom can be circumvented by careful planning. A wise couple will make a point of being ahead of events. They move into a smaller and more convenient house, where public transport is readily available. It is as well not to move away from old friends. Retired people must plan to keep active in mind, body and in social activities. The brain can be stimulated by attending evening classes, or by playing games like chess, dominoes or cards, and reading books and writing letters are also activities to be commended. Browsing through a newspaper and watching television by the hour demand too little effort to be of much use.

Exercise several times a week is necessary, and this can be had in the form of gardening, walking for an hour or two, or swimming. The latter is the best exercise of all. Games such as golf or bowls are also very good, but a leisurely stroll along the seafront, or round the shops for half an hour does not provide enough exercise. Social activities are vital. Friendships are never more important than in old age. They have to be made and maintained, they don't just happen. If some friends are young people, so much the better. These bonds can be forged by joining clubs of all kinds. Members of an active church are assured of companionship. The pensioner has time to work for voluntary associations, and the demand for such community activities has never been greater. It is a good idea for husband and wife to have some pastimes apart, as well as those enjoyed together, as this gives them something to talk about. If people make sensible preparations for this new phase of life, it can be most enjoyable. Retirement should not be equated with old age. The human life-span has increased far beyond the biblical 'three score years and ten'. People should not consider themselves old until they are over eighty, and some lucky people remain vital and active far beyond that age. For those who do fall into the slough of despond, the usual treatments can be applied.

DEPRESSION IN OLD AGE

Advancing years do bring many distressing situations. Not only is there a sapping of physical and mental vitality, but one can see even worse things happening among contemporaries, as death picks them off, one by one. This falling off of the various faculties is summed up in the following doggerel.

'I get by with my bifocals,
To my dentures I'm resigned.
I manage with my deaf aid,
But ye gods, I miss my mind.'

With all these problems, it is not surprising to find that melancholia is a common syndrome in old age. It has been estimated that no less than one in every five of the age group are so afflicted. When these people report to their doctors, they make the most of their physical shortcomings and rarely mention how low and wretched they feel. I have already pointed out that depression is a master of camouflage. A retired coal-miner had a bad cough, was losing weight and looked a very sick man. An X-ray of his chest revealed a shadow and it was assumed he had lung cancer. He went steadily downhill; took to his bed and we all awaited the end. At one visit, his wife told me that before the illness had started, he had behaved in a very strange way. An idle man by nature, he became very active, getting up at five in the morning to work in his garden, and he even had absurd schemes for adopting children. She added that she thought he was getting the mania! This revelation made me have another X-ray taken. The shadow hadn't extended and could have been a benign calcification. He was transferred to a mental hospital where he had electroplexy and made a remarkable recovery. It was the story of that patch of elation that alerted me to the true diagnosis.

The following story is typical of what can happen to an old person in a state of depression. The lady in question was the widow of a farmer, and lived alone in a small house. She was very active, entertained friends and went to her church each Sunday. She had never been ill in her life, only having needed doctors when she had her babies. Her health began to fail, she found she could not cope, and one of her daughters took her into her home. The younger woman was sure it was a matter of old age taking over, but just in case something happened, I was asked to see her mother. I could find no physical illness. She didn't weep, she was not that sort, but under a façade of resignation, I found a very distressed old lady. She had lost a number of old friends and she felt sure she was going the same way. She hated being a nuisance to her children, thinking it would be better if she were dead and out of the way. She was given anti-depressant drugs, and to the surprise of her family, recovered and was able to go back to her own home, and her independent way of life.

Faced with depression in an old person, it is most important that environmental factors should be explored. It is necessary to be aware of any problems, and an attempt should be made to find a solution. A woman and her husband retired to live next door to their daughter. It seemed to be a very good idea, as the younger woman felt it was only a matter of time before her parents would need her help. Her mother was a remarkably fit woman who had just given up her work at the age of 70. Unfortunately she could not settle. She joined the Old People's Fellowship and did her best to integrate into the new community, but without success. She became distressed and miserable. I discussed the situation with her. She said that she had actually given up her job to move, and she was missing her friends from the factory very much indeed. The whole business had been a great mistake. It was difficult to see how the situation could be reversed, and as counselling did no good, I tried her on anti-depressant tablets and she improved. After a few months she asked if she could stop them as she didn't really want to be on pills for the rest of her life. To this I agreed, but she was soon slumped again into a deep state of depression. At this point her husband heard that there was a small council flat going in the village where they were before, some twenty miles away. They moved back and her depression lifted. I have followed her progress closely over the years, and there has been no setback. Solving her basic problem was far more effective and long-term than the administration of drugs; but they had been a useful stopgap.

Depression in old age is such a common malady, it should always be borne in mind. If the old person is suffering from an ill-defined condition, or if counselling and background manipulation don't help, a course of anti-depressant tablets is worth a trial. In severe cases of depression, electroplexy may be necessary.

5
The Art of Counselling

It has already been suggested that with the very mild everyday types of depression, the victim is usually able to solve his problem, or else he learns to adapt and accept the adverse circumstances. If, however, the state of depression lingers on and on, active treatment may be necessary. I would suggest that if the low moods last continuously for more than two weeks, then expert advice should be sought. The local general practitioner is the obvious choice, but doctors certainly don't have a monopoly in the handling of these cases. If a child is depressed, the mother may well seek help from one of his teachers. Some folk may prefer to talk to a minister of religion – clergy who have had training on such matters can be most useful. Women may prefer to seek advice from another woman, and they can talk to the district nurse, the health visitor, or some member of the social services. These people may be able to solve the problem by their wise counselling. This book describes the medical approach.

The art of counselling has as its objective some satisfactory resolution of the client's problem, and this is done by helping him to understand what is going on. If you hold this page too close to your eyes, you won't be able to read a word, but if you move it to about a foot away, the letters come into focus. In much the same way we are sometimes too close to our problems to understand their full significance, and we need the help of a skilled counsellor to see things as they really are. Problems create anxiety, and anxiety is a form of fear prolonged in time. With problem solving, it is necessary to know something about the mechanisms of fear and anxiety, and how they can produce a whole host of physical symptoms, including pain which is real, and certainly not imaginary.

All animals have a wonderful protective mechanism called the fight-flight reaction. Think of a cat sitting on the doorstep enjoying a quiet sleep in the sun. Suddenly a dog appears. The sound, or smell, of the intruder instantly alerts the cat. It may sprint away and climb a tree into safety; or it may hold its ground with an arched back, claws drawn while it hisses defiance at the dog. As far as the cat goes, this alerting mechanism is life saving. Our early ancestors all acquired this safety device, which over the millenia has helped to preserve us as a species. We still have this reaction built into our make-up today, but we don't often have to make use of it as it was intended. We are no longer confronted with cave bears or the sabre-toothed tigers as were our ancestors. In the fight-flight situation the whole mechanism is brought into action by the outpouring of a hormone called adrenalin into the bloodstream. In a matter of a second this alerts the whole body so that it can respond to the situation with maximum efficiency. The pulse quickens to increase blood circulation to the muscles which in turn tone up. Sugar is released from the liver so that they have all the fuel that they need. The pupils of the eye dilate to give better vision, and the skin pales to diminish blood loss in case of injury. Our hair stands on end; in our cousins, the apes, this made them look immensely much bigger and more aggressive. Modern man only rarely meets the acute fear situation, but he is all too often plagued by worries. It may be that he doesn't get on with his foreman at work, or he wonders how he is going to manage on the wages he earns, or perhaps there are marriage difficulties. As a result of such anxiety-provoking problems, instead of a rapid squirt of adrenalin, with worry, the hormone just dribbles into the blood stream, which gives rise to sweating, a fast pulse, breathing upsets and other unpleasant symptoms. The cause of this uncomfortable situation is that the victim is not able to respond in a useful way to the extra adrenalin, and often he is completely unaware that these unpleasant feelings come from the stress he is compelled to endure. Even when circumstances provoke a sudden and violent outpouring of the hormone, the effect can vary as shown in the following two experiences.

I called at a farmhouse one day, to find the front door was locked. As I turned to leave, I saw a large guard dog rushing towards me, with its ears well back. I am a dog lover, but I realised in a flash that this animal meant business, and as there was no way of escape, I just had to fight. With my back to the door, I first lashed out with my right foot, hitting the animal under its jaws. Undeterred by this, it gripped me by the thigh, and I poked a finger hard into one of its eyes. It released me for a moment and drew back, and at that point the farmer arrived and called it off. My thigh injury was minimal, but what surprised me was the feeling of elation that swept over me. I had won the fight!

This response to adrenalin correctly used was very different from when I had a near miss in a car accident. A lorry stopped suddenly, and I had to brake violently. The driver of a car behind had to do the same, and he missed a collision by inches. Furiously angry he leapt out of his vehicle, came round to my window and accused me of almost wrecking his car. There was an immediate surge of adrenalin into my blood, but I could not make good use of it. Argument was useless, so I just closed the window and drove off, but I remained in a state of tension with a tight band round my chest, wondering if I was going to have a heart attack. Inappropriate reactions to the fight-flight mechanism bring considerable bodily discomfort, and to the anxious person, this goes on day after day. Under these circumstances it is hardly surprising that such people think that all the symptoms are due to some physical disease. Attempts to explain this reaction by any over-simplification such as the popular assertion that it's all a question of mind over matter, is far too glib to be convincing. To the worried person, this can be interpreted as implying his symptoms are all just imaginary, which is certainly not the case.

To explain this, I tell the story of the running nose. If you go to a party and there discover you have no handkerchief, at once your nose begins to run, and it is certainly no imaginary drip. It is caused by embarrassment, and it stops as soon as a friend hands over a few tissues.

We can certainly upset the function of the body by paying too much attention to it. If you concentrate on your breathing, you may begin to sigh and have strange feelings in your chest. Some people get worried about this; they think that they are about to stop breathing altogether, and as a result, they over-breathe. This can make the small muscles of the hands and feet go into spasm, which causes further alarm. There is no danger that the breathing mechanism will suddenly fail. This function is automatic and is only upset if a person tries to control it in a voluntary manner.

To unravel a patient's problem is rather like piecing together a jigsaw puzzle; this can be easy, or it can be very complicated and take up hours of time. The first step in the treatment by counselling is to make an accurate assessment of the case. The counsellor will want to explore the background of the trouble over past months or even years, to see what incidents have a bearing on the depression. As a doctor, I carry out a complete physical examination to exclude any possible physical disease. A thorough check-up is likely to increase the patient's confidence in his physician. If a further investigation such as an X-ray is required, it must be completed before any formal sessions of counselling are started. During this consultation, the counsellor will get the feel of the case. I have already described the infectious nature of elation. In the same way the anxious patient exudes his own peculiar aura, and the melancholic brings with him an atmosphere of gloom and doom. The important thing is to listen to the patient, to get him to talk. The whole process of counselling will now be illustrated by a few case histories.

A girl of 18 came to me complaining of a pain in her right upper arm. I could find no physical explanation for her trouble so I went on to tell her that discomfort of this sort could come from nervous tension and that worry itself could cause the pain. At once she asked me to tell her something about cancer. I responded by enquiring what she wanted to know about it. She told me how three weeks before, she had bumped her right breast, and now she could feel a lump in it. I examined her carefully and could find no abnormal swelling. I showed her that by pinching her breast tissue, one could feel a spurious lump, and I demonstrated how to palpate the breast more accurately with the flat of the hand. During the interview I had encouraged her to talk and this helped her to reveal her real worry. In the first instance she had come to see me with a dread of cancer, but she could not bring herself to mention that frightening word, it was much easier to talk about a pain in her arm. She needed a little encouragement to reveal her real problem. I showed her how she had misinterpreted the feel of her breast, and in simple terms I explained how anxiety could produce pain. I told her of a man with a fear of heart disease who had pains in his chest, and of how he had noticed that with that pain, his chest muscles became tense and hard. If, after my examination of her arm, I had told her that there was nothing wrong with her and patted her on the back telling her not to worry, this would have been a futile exercise; she had a great deal on her mind to make her anxious. It was only when the real worry had been exposed and debunked, that she could accept reassurance. When I saw her again two weeks later she told me that all her worries had gone.

Years ago, a woman came to see me and asked for a tonic as for some time she had felt vaguely unwell. On questioning she revealed that for some six months she had been feeling depressed and miserable. She was given to bouts of crying, and she could not sleep at nights. Her story was as follows. In the early stages of the war she had been bombed out of her home in Coventry and she and her two children had been evacuated to the country where she had been lucky enough to find a small cottage which she did not have to share. Her husband was in the army, and had been sent out to Egypt. During the war years she had made the best of life in the country, but now that hostilities were over, she wanted to get back to her home town. She had applied to the authorities in Coventry, but had been told that as she already had a house, she was ineligible for accommodation in that city. In the mean time her husband had been home on leave, but was still awaiting demobilisation. She was now pregnant, and looking forward to having another baby. It was the outright rejection she had had from Coventry that had got her down, and after years of loneliness while separated from her husband, she was longing to get back to a normal life in her own home town. After half an hour of discussion, she told me she felt better for having got things off her chest, and she was greatly cheered when I told her I would write to the authorities. It was obvious that with her husband and the new baby, the cottage would be too small. My letter bore fruit, and three months later she moved back to Coventry. She wrote after the birth of her child to tell me that she had never felt better in her life. In this simple case, a sympathetic ear combined with a manipulation of circumstances brought about a recovery from a straightforward reactive depression.

Unfortunately, one can only rarely alter the environment in this way. As a rule, the best one can do is to help the patient to come to terms with life. A man of considerable character had worked as a deputy down the coal-mines, but he was a man of many parts; an elder in his church, a local councillor and on the village bowls team. He came to see me because he felt his nerves were in a bad way. He could not sleep at night, and in consequence was finding work a strain. He felt that he was losing his grip on the men under him. All his working hours he was convinced something awful was going to happen; he went into a panic when the telephone rang. He was so depressed that he wept as he told me his story. His past history was indeed a tale of woe. It was two years since he had lost his wife from cancer, and he had been left with three young sons to look after. His family had never approved of his marriage and were offhand and unsympathetic. They had never once visited his wife when she was ill. It was with some hesitation that he told me of another trouble. His eldest son, a boy of 18, had got a girl pregnant, and what had grieved him most was that he had been told the news by the girl's father. He blamed himself, as he felt he had lost his son's confidence. All in all it was clear that not only did he feel he was losing his grip with the men at work, but also with his family at home. Talking with me gave him the urge to talk things over with his son man-to-man and together they decided on a plan of action. He came to me for some four counselling sessions, and after that he was able to manage on his own. I had helped him to recover his self-respect and his ability to manage his own affairs.

The cases I have described so far have been fairly simple ones that were solved by a minimum of counselling and support. Some people need longer term treatment and the following case shows what extended therapy can do.

A young soldier had been repatriated from the Middle East because he had become 'bomb happy' and was considered unfit for active service. On his return to South Africa, he had been given sick leave, and during that time he got married. He was then posted as a clerk to a training unit in the Transvaal. He became too ill to manage his work and it was from there that he came under my care in a military hospital. The youth was convinced that he had a bad heart and he was expecting to drop dead at any moment. He described his attacks as being overcome by a wave of terror; his heart began to pound and he felt as if there was an iron band round his chest. He could hardly breathe. A complete physical examination had revealed no sign of any heart trouble, but this was no consolation to him. He just could not believe it. I discovered that his first attack had come on when he was travelling home on a train for a spell of leave. He was about to be re-united with his wife. While we were discussing what had happened to him, he told me he thought it was the beer that had upset him. I asked for more details, and he went on to say that the night before he left the unit, he and his friends had had a party to celebrate his leave. He came from a puritanical family, who were strictly teetotal, but on this occasion he had been tempted by the boys to have a few pints of beer. In fact he had got blind drunk, and was thoroughly ashamed of himself. He then added that there were girls at the party, and after that admission he suddenly dried up. It required considerable encouragement to get him to continue. Reluctantly he admitted that it was just possible that he had seduced one of the girls, and then he added hastily he thought that event had just been a dream. He had thrown in the dream idea as a smokescreen, but it seemed clear that on the night before a joyful reunion with his wife, he had been unfaithful to her, and he went home laden with feelings of guilt. Suddenly on the train he had managed to replace that painful memory with all its remorse by a so-called heart attack, and the fear of dying. In the short term this exchange was profitable. His wife was sorry for him and loved him more than ever, but, had she known the truth, her reaction would have been very different. I had to delve even further back into his history to discover the basis for his heart fears. During his time in the Western Desert, he had grown more and more alarmed by air attacks from the Germans. At one time he was lying in a slit trench, when the area was sprayed with bullets which were close enough to scatter sand over him. When a few minutes later they were dive-bombed by a Stuka, he went into a panic, and the primitive flight mechanism took over. He jumped out of his trench and ran across the desert until he could run no further, and then he fell sobbing into another slit trench. He fully realised at the time that he had behaved like a coward, and he dreaded what his companions would say to him. He was eventually picked up and sent back for a medical assessment. He was labelled as being 'bomb happy' and returned to South Africa. He was not proud of that panic reaction, and he fully admitted he had been 'yellow'. The whole incident filled him with feelings of guilt – he was a poor soldier and had let the side down. Some eighteen months later his conscience was again damaged by his infidelity. This time he tried to cover up his feelings by having a so-called heart attack, which was in fact a complete replica of how he felt in the slit trench, when for the first time he had been overwhelmed by feelings of guilt. I was able, step by step, to get him to look objectively at what had happened, and to put the blame where it rightly belonged. His heart fears had helped him to get round the reunion with his wife, without any loss of her affection, but in the long run, the bargain was a bad one. He lived in terror of his life, convinced that at any moment he would drop dead. In the end he was able to accept that his heart was not at fault, and that he was suffering from a very guilty conscience. He left hospital much better after some four weeks of treatment.

Endogenous depression can present as an anxiety reaction. It is not always easy to differentiate between these two depressive states. A married man of 34 came to see me with a pain in his chest. As he had lost his father some six months earlier from a heart attack, I suspected he had a fear of cardiac disease. I could find no physical evidence of this, so I decided to try and unravel some of his problems by persuading him to talk. After a second session, his wife rang me up to ask me what I thought of him. When I explained what I was attempting to do, she said she was extremely worried about him. She went on to say that before she was married, she had worked for a boss who had committed suicide, and she felt her husband was heading the same way. I asked her to bring him along the same evening. Further exploration convinced me that the wife was right; he was far more depressed than I had at first realised. I told him what I thought and how I proposed to treat him. He agreed to co-operate and after a couple of weeks on anti-depressant drugs his heart worries and his morbid thoughts disappeared.

I make it a rule that having done my best to assess a case, if the diagnosis remains in doubt as to whether the depression was purely reactive, or a possible endogenous type, I treat the problem as being endogenous. The drugs we use for depression can do no harm, whereas to miss an endogenous depression could be dangerous. The timely intervention of the last patient's wife may well have saved his life.

Trained lay counsellors are quite capable of helping people suffering from a reactive depression. Each therapist has his own way of dealing with such patients. However if there is any suggestion that the depression could be endogenous, then the client must be passed on to a doctor who can prescribe any drugs that may be necessary. It is of the utmost importance that lay therapists should be aware of endogenous depression and be able to recognise it, so that such clients can receive appropriate medical treatment. Quite recently, a brilliant young friend of mine approached his parish priest about a personal problem. He saw him frequently, and even rang him up at four o'clock in the morning for advice. Unfortunately the cleric failed to spot that the intense anxiety sprang from a severe endogenous depression, and the result was that the young man killed himself. Severe anxiety, often over-demanding in character, is usually a symptom of endogenous depression, and as such demands urgent physical treatment.

There is another danger inherent in counselling. It is a great comfort to be able to talk over problems with a kindly sympathetic person, and the client can become addicted to the treatment. A skilled therapist will see that this does not happen.

6
Physical Methods of Treatment

CHEMICAL IMBALANCE

Manic depressive disease can be compared with gout. Both are maladies that come out of the blue, and often attacks are repeated at intervals. Both diseases are caused by a chemical upset in the way the body functions. Most of us get rid of the waste product, uric acid, by flushing it away in the urine. In a victim of gout, the body periodically allows an accumulation of uric acid to occur, and it is deposited as sharp crystals in certain joints, which then become excruciatingly painful. This process can be reversed or even prevented from happening by prescribing certain chemical agents. A comparable reaction in the body chemistry causes endogenous depression, but here the precise mechanism is not so clear, and it is certainly not as simple as the adrenalin response to fear and anxiety. With melancholia we know that there is an imbalance of compounds called catecholamines, and this deviation from the norm can cause depression, or more rarely, mania. This process can be reversed by the administration of certain drugs, of which there are a large variety.

Anti-depressant Drugs

These potent agents became available in the late 1950s. Before then, the only treatment to abolish depression was electroplexy, which was often only available to the patient who agreed to be admitted to the local mental hospital – no easy option for a melancholic who found it hard enough

64

to drag himself down to the doctor's surgery. However, once the new drugs came on the market, melancholics could be treated in their own home, without any reference to the psychiatric services. In Britain, a visit to a psychiatrist, or treatment in a psychiatric institution, carries with it a certain social stigma. It can bar a person from joining the police force or one of the armed services, and it can be a barrier to emigration. Being treated at home by one's family doctor produces no such blemish to the reputation. Depression is an illness, and many melancholics when they are well are the most worthy of citizens. There should be no stigma attached to the illness, but it does occur. In the USA, people have no such fear of the psychiatrist. For those who can afford his fees, he has much the same status as the parish priest. Both are professionals whose advice is eagerly sought by certain sections of the community, when confronted by a problem.

The first case I treated with these new drugs was a man who had suffered from manic depressive disease most of his working life. He was an architect by profession. His wife had found life with him and his mood changes so intolerable that she had committed suicide. In a state of deep depression, he returned to his native village and was living with his aged parents. He sat by the fire all day doing nothing. I had to visit him from time to time to give him his sick certificate. He refused point blank to see a psychiatrist or to go to the local mental hospital. When the new drugs became available, I asked him if he would take them, and to this he agreed. To my amazement, some ten days later he appeared at my surgery with plans he had drawn up for a bungalow he intended to have built. He had not been out of the house for months. I felt compelled to make some comments on his drawings, so I suggested a few minor changes. That evening he was back at the surgery again with a completely new set of plans, into which he had incorporated all my suggestions. The drug had clearly raised him into a state of productive elation. This dramatic recovery convinced me that these drugs really did work. I had at that time a sizeable quota of depressed patients attending the surgery, and in most of these I witnessed a similar response to that of the architect. One woman, who had been housebound for years, started going to church again, and living a normal social life.

The discovery of anti-depressant drugs made as much impact on my work in psychiatry as had the antibiotics in the field of infectious diseases. In some ways these two groups of drugs are comparable. Both agents are selective. We use one form of antibiotic to treat a sore throat and another to combat tuberculosis. In much the same way the doctor has to choose the correct form of anti-depressant for each patient he sees, and the patient needs to know what the drug will do to him. There is one big difference between these two groups of medicaments. Antibiotics act pretty quickly and a good result is obvious in a few days, whereas the anti-depressant agents are slow acting and there can be a frustrating ten to fourteen day interval before any benefit is felt by the patient. He may even feel worse because of the side effects. During that time the melancholic needs a considerable amount of support.

He must learn to accept the side effects and to put up with an increase in the mood swings, which are an indication that the depression is breaking up. The analogy of fell walking is useful to patients. When one climbs a mountain, there are always a few false summits. The rambler thinks he is at the top, only to find himself on a hump, with the real summit seemingly as far away as ever. He may even have to go down a bit before he starts to climb again, but his disappointment can be mitigated if he looks backwards. He can then see how far he has climbed.

The diagram on page 24 illustrates a typical course for an endogenous depression. The normal everyday mood swings, which occur in all of us, give way to much more dramatic changes, and each day the low feelings persist longer and get slowly worse. Once the nadir of the melancholia is reached, these variations tend to flatten out, with the patient at his lowest ebb in the mornings, and somewhat better by night-fall. This can continue for weeks or months, and then the exaggerated mood swings return, heralding a recovery. Once normality has been reached this may well extend into a period of elation, sometimes amounting to hypomania. The moods then slowly settle back to the normal rhythm. Drug treatment pushes up the mood in a matter of ten days, but the medication needs to be maintained until a normal remission would have occurred.

It is beyond the scope of this book to go into the minute details of drug treatment, but a brief guide to therapy may be helpful. These agents can be divided into three groups.

1 The Tricyclics

These include the original drugs introduced in the late 1950s. They are slow to disperse the depression, and initially can make the patient feel even worse, because of the side effects. These reactions can be minimised by starting on a small dose and building up to the full amount over a period of a week. The full dose needs to be kept up for a whole week before any real benefit can be felt from the treatment. Drowsiness and an unpleasant feeling of detachment wear off after a while, but some of the side effects persist for as long as the drug is taken. These include a dry mouth, weight gain and constipation (the last symptom can be eased by taking plenty of bran with a breakfast cereal). Tiresome as these symptoms are, once the drug is having the desired effect of lifting the depression, most patients are well prepared to accept these unpleasant reactions.

2 Monoamine Oxidase Inhibitors

This is usually abbreviated to the initials MAOI. All these drugs necessitate a special diet, from which certain food items are excluded. The patient must not eat cheese, yeast extracts, herrings or drink red wine. People on these agents are given a card to detail the things that have to be avoided. This group of drugs can initially be even more unpleasant to take than the tricyclics; but on the other hand they can have quite dramatically good effects once the therapeutic dose is reached. One young man felt so well that he was worried in case he could ever manage without his tablets. His anxiety was ill-founded, as after some three months he was able to drop them without any relapse. Because of the side effects, it is essential to build up to a full dose slowly, usually over some three or four weeks. The patient needs considerable encouragement to stick to the treatment, but once an adequate dosage has been reached, the side effects become less. One tiresome problem can be weight gain, which is sometimes difficult to counter even with dieting.

3 Other New Drugs

There are other drugs now available that do not have so many side effects, and which seem to raise the depression quicker, but they are not suitable for all types of cases. They are sometimes referred to as second generation antidepressants.

Another medicament available is lithium. This can be very effective in mania, and it is also useful in patients who are liable to recurrent attacks of depression. I treated a woman who had been plagued with the illness for almost forty years, during which time she was frequently admitted to hospital. As soon as she started on lithium, she ceased to have attacks, and has now been free from them for some fifteen years. With this agent, regular blood tests are essential, as the correct level of lithium in the blood must be maintained.

Each patient with depression is different from other melancholics, and the choice of treatment by the doctor is based on various features in the illness of that particular patient. If the first drug tried is not successful, another is used on its own or in combination with the first. Occasionally it can take quite a long time to find the ideal therapy for a particular patient. However, with doctor and patient working together, the vast majority of depressed people can be rescued from their vale of misery.

On the other hand it must be admitted that the perfect remedy has not yet been found. Side effects are not peculiar to anti-depressant drugs. Don't forget that with most surgical operations, the patient has to put up with considerable pain and inconvenience before a full recovery is attained.

Untreated, endogenous depression is a self-limiting illness in most cases. On average it lasts for the best part of a year, which is a very long time to feel desolate and in misery. Anti-depressant drugs remove the symptoms of the illness, but they have to be taken until the natural rhythm and production of the catecholamines have returned to normal, and this can mean taking them for anything from three months to a year or more. The side effects have one very useful function in that the patient is only too glad to stop them, once the doctor has given his consent for this to happen. In other words, people don't become addicted to these drugs.

Because of its function as a preventive agent, lithium may have to be taken indefinitely.

Tranquillisers and Sleeping Tablets

There is a group of drugs known as tranquillisers which have been used to allay anxiety. They are no remedy for the depressed patient. As an anti-anxiety agent, they have a useful function in an emergency. The woman who has been devastated by the sudden loss of her husband may be helped over the first week of her bereavement by such medicaments, but prolonged courses are counterproductive as the patient so readily becomes addicted to the agent, and they tend to impair judgement.

For example, if a woman who is relying on such drugs were to come home early from work one day to find her husband in bed with the girl from next door, instead of blowing her top in no uncertain manner (which would be the normal reaction), she might well just sneak off and take an overdose of aspirins.

In short sharp courses, tranquillisers can be very useful, and if the patient is told when they have been prescribed that they are just for a week, the idea is usually accepted without question. There is no short cut to the allaying of anxiety by way of drug treatment; the listening ear of the counsellor is a far more important remedy.

Insomnia is a common symptom of both worry and depression, but unfortunately there is no drug available that can reproduce natural sleep. All that has been said about the addictive qualities of tranquillisers applies to sleeping tablets. They may have a place in an emergency situation for patients who request them, but they are no answer to chronic insomnia. Taken for any length of time, they lose their effect and the patient is tempted to take them in increasing doses. These drugs produce a modified form of anaesthesia which leaves the patient with a morning hangover. This may not amount to the blinding headache which can follow a heavy alcoholic party, but it does leave the brain functioning below par the next day. Much the same applies to alcohol. A nightcap of spirits may help some people to sleep, but it has the opposite effect on others, and the habit has the same addictive property as the sleeping tablet.

Lack of sleep on its own does no harm. Volunteers who have been deprived of sleep for a few days recover after a single night's rest. They will need a few hours longer than their normal resting time but that is all. It is not a lack of sleep that does the harm, but worrying about the habit that causes the trouble. If a person can be persuaded to put up with a few bad nights without getting alarmed about it, normal sleep usually returns. There are a number of safe first aid methods that can be tried. Tea and coffee should be avoided in the evenings, but hot milky drinks sometimes help. It is important not to go to bed too early, and reading a book when one has retired for the night may help one to relax. There are many things that prevent sound sleep, such as an uncomfortable bed, cold, anxiety or loneliness. These should be investigated and, if possible, corrected. Old people who move into sheltered accommodation often state that they sleep far better knowing that there are other people near at hand.

Electroplexy

A Hungarian psychiatrist was the first doctor to use what is called convulsive therapy. He caused the fits by giving his patients an injection of camphor. The method was crude and extremely unpleasant for the recipient. It was soon superseded by a method which involved passing a short sharp electric current through the brain. This system was a big advance, but still had its disadvantages. During the convulsions that followed the shock, bones could be broken, and patients were frightened and apprehensive about the treatment.

These difficulties have been largely overcome by employing an anaesthetist, who gives the patient an injection to relax the muscles, and then puts him to sleep by means of a quick-acting barbiturate anaesthetic which makes the patient pass out in a split second. This method of anaesthesia is not at all unpleasant; a big advance from the bad old days when one was suffocated by chloroform or ether, and took several minutes to become unconscious. The patient who has electroplexy today has nothing to worry about; it is both painless and safe. In the treatment of depression it has certain advantages over drug treatment, but like drug therapy it has a side effect, namely that the patient is left with transient holes in the memory. An eminent physician I know

71

well has had many courses of this treatment, and he has assured me that the memory soon recovers. The treatment has certainly had no untoward effect on his medical career.

This treatment is indicated when drugs have failed to give relief to the patient, or when the sick person is so ill that he urgently requires measures to bring about a rapid recovery. Electroplexy works more quickly than anti-depressant drugs, and the return to normal is usually sustained; but a few patients do need additional drug therapy until such time as the chemical balance of the brain has been restored. Today, only a small minority of depressed people need this form of treatment, and it can be given on an out-patient basis at any psychiatric clinic. No one knows exactly how the treatment works, but few practising psychiatrists would care to operate without it being available in the appropriate case.

The following experience convinced me that electroplexy really did work. A married woman with four little girls called me one Monday morning to see the youngest child who had had a pain in her stomach since the Saturday. The mother had not sent for a doctor as she didn't want to disturb any of us over the weekend. The child had a ruptured appendix and was sent to hospital, but she died a few days later. The mother slowly sank into a deep depression. I saw her several times for counselling sessions, but they didn't help her. She kept telling me that she could never forgive herself, as she had killed her own child. I explained to her that we all make foolish mistakes at times, and usually we get away with it. She had been unlucky and her error had ended in disaster. She remained inconsolable, and then one day she said she was beginning to hate the other girls as they reminded her of the one she had lost. I felt that drastic measures were necessary and advised her to have a course of electroplexy at the local mental hospital. To my relief, she agreed to this advice.

When I saw her again a few weeks later, this mother was quite a different woman. She told me she now accepted that

72

she had made a grave mistake, but the thought of what had happened no longer dominated her life. As she put it, she had begun to live again. She went on to say that when she went into the hospital, she had absolutely no hope that any treatment would do her the slightest bit of good; she had only agreed to accept it as I had been so kind to her. I followed her up over many years and she never had a relapse. Electroplexy seems to be able to stop morbid thoughts from going round and round in the mind of the patient.

7
Other Roads to Recovery

While I was a general practitioner, I instituted a long-term study of depressive disorders and was surprised at the number of cases of endogenous depression that came my way. I was concerned that I might be over-diagnosing the condition, so I referred as many patients as I could to psychiatrists, who invariably agreed with my opinion. This made me realise that the problem was far bigger than was generally appreciated, either by the public, or the medical profession.

I was able to deal with patients suffering from reactive depressions, but counselling is always a very time-consuming task. With cases of endogenous depression, the situation was somewhat different. Those who were very ill were in some ways lucky, as by admitting them to the local mental hospital, they could get the electroplexy they needed, and they recovered. The mild and moderate cases had to be supported at home. I could only offer them encouragement and symptomatic treatment. To allay insomnia, they were given barbituates, and to alert them in the mornings, I used various forms of amphetamine drugs. The medicaments used then would never be supplied today. They helped in a very limited way, but in no way cut short the illness.

In 1947 in 'Endogenous Depression in General Practice' (*BMJ* I, 11) I reported on some twenty cases of endogenous depression I had diagnosed; most of them had been ill for months, and one for no less than two and a half years. The recovery of these people seemed to be deplorably slow. Eleven of the group claimed to be back to normal, including a man who had been ill for years.

When anti-depressant drugs became easily available, my

treatment was revolutionised, and for a while, I was deluded into thinking that at last we were getting down to solving the entire problem of depression, especially with the co-operation and back-up of a good family to help the patient through his convalescence.

THE ROLE OF THE FAMILY

The rest of the family has a very important part to play in the care of the depressed patient. Sometimes the melancholic is quite reluctant to see a doctor, and in these circumstances the relatives must insist on a medical opinion. If, having made an appointment at the surgery, the patient refuses to keep it, then the doctor should be asked to call and see the patient at home. It is important to explain to the general practitioner that the patient is reluctant to see him. Whatever the arrangement, it must be done openly with the patient knowing what is happening; he must not be deceived in any way. There is certainly no place for saying that the doctor just happened to be passing, and dropped in for a chat. The same candour must be used when introducing a psychiatrist, if such a consultant has been called in for a second opinion. He must be labelled as a psychiatrist, and not by any misleading euphemism.

With tactful handling, most depressed people are only too willing to talk to the doctor, especially if the path has been made easy for them. It is essential that the doctor should keep the family informed as to what is going on, so that they can support the sick person. They must see that medicine is taken regularly as prescribed. They must listen sympathetically to the patient's grumbles and complaints. More often than not, the patient, when well, is a conscientious and hardworking type. He is only too aware of the fact that his efficiency has dropped off, and to be told by friends and relatives to pull himself together is more than a little hurtful.

For weeks he has been trying to do just that, and he can no more snap out of it than he can lift himself into the air by pulling on his shoelaces. The correct way to meet the patient's grumbles or strange ideas is to say they are all due to his illness, and that now he is under treatment, they will soon pass. Such reassurances may have to be repeated again and again, and in spite of apparent apathy on the part of the patient, they do help. Before drugs were available, this was all I could offer week after week, assuring the victim that in time the low moods would pass. Once they had recovered, many of these patients told me how comforting my reassurances had been.

The main danger of depression is suicide. It is a popular belief that if a person threatens to kill himself, he will never do it. This is a very dangerous fallacy. Any talk of suicide must be taken seriously, and this fear should be conveyed at once to the family doctor. Relatives have an uncanny knack of assessing the patient's suicidal tendencies. A doctor should always tactfully ask questions on this matter, and if there is any risk, make a point of telling the next of kin. They will invariably reply that they are aware of the danger, and have not left the patient alone for weeks.

The woman described in Chapter 5 who had worked with a boss who killed himself, realised there was a suicidal risk with her husband, and very wisely drew my attention to this. Once active treatment has been established, the danger from suicide rapidly gets less. Most patients who have a suicidal urge are best treated in hospital; indeed some of my depressed clients have actually asked me to get them into a psychiatric ward, as there they felt more secure. There are, however, exceptions to this rule. One Christmas Eve two worried young men brought their father to see me. They had found him making preparations to hang himself. Just before Christmas was not the easiest time to find a hospital bed, so I talked to the patient at some length, and was able to put across to him that he was a sick man, and that his illness was

76

treatable. He agreed to accept all my advice and take a course of anti-depressant tablets. With his caring family round him, I sent him home and he went on to make a good recovery.

Sometimes the depressed person makes sudden and unwise decisions. I have already described in Chapter 4 how a young woman wanted to call off her marriage. A farmer moved into a new area, and after a few weeks in the district sank into a deep state of depression. He decided that his move had been a great mistake, and he was all for selling his business. Had he done so, he would have lost a great deal of money. I persuaded him to delay a final decision until he had had treatment for his depression. He made a good recovery, and thirty years later he is a very successful farmer. Relatives must support the idea of putting off any vital decision until the depression has been treated. With recovery, the original ideas are usually forgotten.

Another function of the family is to ensure that at the end of any treatment, the patient has returned fully to normal. The sick person who has made a partial recovery may well feel it would be churlish to complain that she is not completely well. Not every one is as wise as one lady who was one of the first batch of patients to be treated by drugs, and improved rapidly. After some two months during a consultation she told me that she didn't wish to appear ungrateful, but while she was much better, her recovery was not complete; she was only eighty per cent well, and she didn't want to spend the rest of her life like that. Increasing the dose of her medication did not help, so she submitted herself to a short course of electroplexy, and that did the trick. She has had no further breakdown. The family is usually in a better position than either the patient or the doctor to help in the assessment as to how far the patient has reached in the climb back to normality.

Relatives can be most useful as spotters of a depressive illness. This may be difficult with the person who is having his first attack, but with those who have recurrent episodes, recognising the onset can be easy, and very helpful. Some people who are liable to melancholia are prepared to see their doctor as soon as they realise they are sinking into misery; but such people are the exception rather than the rule. The invalid tends to put off the admission that she is ill and keeps on telling herself that this time she will master the illness on her own. *This is certainly not a good idea.*

A very sensible woman, who had been successfully treated for her first attack, was brought along by her husband after she had been ill for some six weeks. She told me tearfully that she had felt such a feeble creature in her low mood, that she was determined to show her mettle by demonstrating that she could master the illness without help. I easily persuaded her to take another course of drugs, and she was soon well again. Before I finally discharged her from my care, she asked me if it wasn't possible to fight depression without medical help. Obviously she was still convinced that if only she had the willpower, she would be able to dispel her misery; she dearly wanted to stand on her own feet, and for that I admired her. However, my advice was that if ever she felt down again for two consecutive weeks, it was time to seek a consultation with me, to allow me to assess the situation.

With people who are unwilling to complain, the relatives must shoulder the responsibility of seeking advice from an expert. It is certainly not a good idea to let a depression run its course. They will often know all the signs of impending depression. This may be in a changed voice, most marked over the telephone, an increase in irritability, or some mannerism, such as playing with the teeth. A few patients give a warning, by having a transient period of elation and over-activity.

Finally, relatives should see that during the period of recovery, the patient lives as normal a life as possible. It is not a good idea to lie in bed all day, but too much activity soon exhausts the patient. She must be encouraged to get up at a reasonable hour, and daily to take some gentle exercise. She should be persuaded to pay attention to her appearance; a visit to a hairdresser can be very beneficial. It is important to see that meals are taken regularly. If she decides to prepare the food, she should be encouraged to do so, and for each step forward, she deserves congratulations. With modern treatment, this kind of support is only necessary for a few days. Words of appreciation will help to raise the morale.

THE CHRONICALLY SICK PATIENT

When anti-depressant drugs had been in use for a few years, I realised that there were still some patients who did not respond to any of the available treatment. Thanks to medical advances, my recovery rate had risen from fifty-five per cent in 1947 to something like eighty per cent in 1970. While this improvement was gratifying, it also meant that some twenty per cent of the psychiatric casualties under my care still defied the best treatment available in both general practice and psychiatric hospitals. There was certainly no room for complacency. These chronic cases made life miserable for themselves and their families, and no conscientious doctor likes to feel impotent to help so many of his patients. Here are a couple of examples.

One married woman was just such a case. Her younger daughter had been killed in a motor accident, and she was overcome with grief and remorse. After many months of mourning, her husband insisted on her seeing me, and I spent some time in counselling sessions. They did no good, so I tried her on some anti-depressant drugs and she began to improve. Her husband was delighted with her progress. Then she decided to drop the drugs and at once became as depressed as ever, and we could not persuade her to restart the treatment. She was referred to a psychiatrist who suggested a course of electroplexy. At first she refused to accept the treatment, then agreed to have it, but as soon as she seemed to be on the mend, she defaulted again, and she remained in a state of depression until she died some five years later.

In a large practice such as ours, there were a number of comparable cases; patients who had attended the surgery regularly year after year, without anyone being able to solve their problems. This group was made up of all sorts of psychiatric illness. There were cases of chronic depression or anxiety, so-called personality disorders, and a few burnt-out schizophrenics.

Another patient's troubles began when she was seventeen. At a party of young people, for the first time in her life she allowed herself to be petted and kissed, and she was convinced that as a result she was going to have a baby. There were no pregnancy tests in those days, but for nine months she was in misery, and thoroughly ashamed of herself for having disgraced her family. At the end of that time, she did concede she had been wrong, but she produced another set of symptoms for which my partner could find no explanation or cure. This fear of disease in one form or another went on continuously. In spite of all her complaints, she had managed to find a long-suffering husband; but they had no children. She was handed over into my care. When I first saw her she was complaining of indigestion, and she was sure she had cancer of the stomach. X-rays showed that organ to be perfectly normal, so I tackled the problem by a series of counselling sessions. These did no good, and when I suggested that she saw a psychiatrist, she refused such a consultation and was hurt by the implications. I continued to see and support her as best I could. For a few months she ceased to see me and then she came along to tell me she was developing poliomyelitis, and she lived in fear that she might be infecting her neighbours. To cut a long story short, she went from one set of depressive delusions to another. At one point she saw a psychiatrist and had a course of electroplexy, but that did not help her, nor did any anti-depressant drugs. Widowed, she ended her days in a warden-supervised set of flatlets. There she was convinced men were prying on her through the windows. What a dreadful life that poor woman had suffered for some sixty years. Doctors certainly don't know *all* the answers to psychiatric illness.

Some fifteen years ago, my attention was drawn to a number of self-help organisations that offered the hand of friendship and gave some hope of recovery to this chronic type of patient. It was an entirely new approach. Such associations encourage patients to meet and talk with fellow sufferers, and members of each group are prepared to offer tender loving care in a lavish manner, indeed on a scale quite impossible for any of the professionals. A study of their various methods has made me realise that they may well bring about recovery in cases such as those above whose problems are so difficult to overcome.

The emergence of self-help groups is timely, while health authorities are returning patients from psychiatric institutions, back into the community. It is now realised that the vast old Victorian asylums were so impersonal that they created chronicity among their clients by the sheer monotony of life inside those high walls. Under such conditions close personal relationships were almost impossible, and the degradation to which so many of the patients were subjected, caused them as much trouble as the disease for which they had been admitted.

To understand this apparent neglect, one must review the history of medicine over the past two centuries. At the beginning of the nineteenth century, doctors had made little progress for several centuries. This situation is illustrated by the fact that the works of Aurelius Celsus, who wrote a treatise on medicine in 30AD, were still recommended reading in 1830! Today a medical textbook is likely to be out of date in ten years. Real advances began in about 1850 when the new skills acquired by surgeons far outpaced those of the physicians. The invention of anaesthesia and antiseptic techniques were the basis of this dramatic progress, and then the discovery of insulin in 1922 heralded a whole spate of discoveries which strengthened the arm of the physician. This trickle of discoveries became a torrent during and after the Second World War. Scientific medicine seemed about to offer a remedy for most human ills.

Unfortunately, psychiatry lagged far behind in this renaissance. The causes of mental illness remained obscure, and apart from electroplexy virtually no new remedies were available. Because of this, psychiatry became the Cinderella of the medical sciences. Real progress in psychiatric care only became apparent around the middle of this century, and this developed along two lines. First there was the impetus given by the discovery of powerful new medicaments such as the anti-depressant drugs, and secondly, a more humane attitude towards the patients was emerging. Closed wards were thrown open, restrictions were eased, and the concept of caring for many of the psychiatric patients in the community developed. All these improvements were steps in the right direction, but it has meant that after-care services have had their resources stretched to the limit. This dangerous situation was well illustrated by a patient who found himself recovering from a severe mental breakdown. When discharged from hospital he was told that in the future he would have to rely on community services. This advice, he suggested, was like flinging a man into a stormy sea, and at the same time telling him a lifeboat would be along later (Manic Depressive Fellowship, 1987, Personal Communication). It is very fortunate that just when the authorities are trying to implement the concept of community care, many self-help organisations have been created and these bodies are only too willing to share the responsibility.

WHERE TO GO FOR HELP

As I have already pointed out, the obvious person to initiate the treatment of a depressed person is the family doctor. Unfortunately there are a few doctors who still seem unaware of the common nature of depressive syndromes, and such people do not have the right temperament for handling these cases. In these circumstances where can the melancholic or his family turn for help?

Nowadays doctors usually work in teams, and it is very unlikely that all the physicians in the group will be unsuitable for the management of a depressed patient. The sick person can thus seek the advice of a more sympathetic doctor direct, or he can explain the situation to the practice nurse or a health visitor who will give advice as to the best medical person to approach. In cases such as this, where rather more time is needed than the standard allocation of five to ten minutes, it is as well to write a letter to the doctor and explain the situation, so that he knows in advance what it is all about and can reserve the necessary time for an assessment.

The Social Services

Every town of any size has an office for the social services, with a telephone number in the directory. Any patient with a problem he is reluctant to discuss with his general practitioner, may be able to get the advice he needs from this organisation. Social workers have training in mental health, and are at least capable of directing the sick person on to the correct path.

The Clergy

Some depressed people gravitate towards a minister of religion. This applies especially to those who have feelings of guilt, and people who are mourning. Here they may get just the counselling they need, or they may be advised as to where to seek medical aid.

The Samaritans

There is a branch of this organisation in every big town, with a telephone number in the directory. The telephone is manned day and night, and anyone wanting a sympathetic ear can ring the Samaritans. Few problems can be solved there and then on a telephone, but arrangements will be made for the client to see some counsellor or a professional without delay. These helpers are able to befriend, but they are more a diagnostic centre than a source of active treatment. It is their job to direct the client to where he can get the help he needs, and this they do most efficiently.

MIND

This organisation was early in the field, battling to improve the services provided for the mentally ill. Their objective was very much to the point. Looking back over the years, it is obvious that many people suffering from depression and other psychiatric disorders did in fact have a raw deal. MIND pulled no punches in pointing out defects in the system. It is now a nationwide organisation in England and Wales with headquarters in London, and branches in most urban communities. MIND aims to see the vast outmoded psychiatric hospitals abolished before the end of the century, to be replaced by a more caring form of service.

MIND offers help to people who are mentally ill in a number of ways. Branches will advise those who need it as to where to look for help with their problems, which may be medical, social such as housing or accommodation, or financial. They can direct patients on how to claim all the benefits due to them. This organisation publishes books, reports and leaflets. Their Fact Sheet on depression is full of useful material and advice. In many areas they run self-help groups where patients can meet and discuss problems with their fellows, and be given the useful support that so many of them need.

Depressives Associated

This self-help group was formed specifically to help persons suffering from the depressive syndromes by putting sufferers in touch with each other by personal contact, letter or telephone. Of these liaisons, the face-to-face meetings are likely to give the most help. The best work is done by local group meetings where mutual problems are aired and discussed. The staff at headquarters will send their literature to any who seek their assistance, and they will advise as to where the nearest group holds its meetings. The association co-operates fully with the professionals, and they offer help and advice to relatives who are often in need of support. Melancholics, ex-sufferers and relatives are encouraged to join the association. Those who have recovered are most welcome as they have so much to offer. Their experience of depression and just how they climbed back to normality can be of the greatest help to people who are actually suffering from a depression. The association issues a quarterly newsletter.

Manic Depressive Fellowship

As I have already suggested, manic-depressive disease is a comparatively rare malady, comprising something like four per cent of the total case load of depressive disorders. It can, however, be a bigger burden for family units to bear than pure depression. The violent mood swings in the sufferer make it extremely hard for relatives to adjust to the ever-changing situation. Under these circumstances, it is useful to have a self-help body prepared to study this particular problem, and to offer support to the families involved. While mania can give transient satisfaction to the patient, it is sheer hell for the family concerned. Treatment by lithium salts solves the problem for most of these patients, but this fellowship has discovered that there is a sizeable minority of cases who resist all forms of treatment at present available. To this unfortunate minority the Manic Depressive Fellowship must be a great help. Their facilities consist of group meetings, pen-friends, a newsletter and information sheets which are available from their headquarters.

Cruse

About the time that anti-depressant drugs became available, in the late 1950s, Margaret Torrie, supported by her psychiatrist husband, formed this organisation to help advise and support widows in their bereavement. At that time, beyond offering such people a pension, which was often inadequate, little was done to help this group of people by the community at large. The name 'Cruse' is derived from a bible story. During a famine, the prophet Elijah asked a poor widow woman to bake him a cake, and this she did with the last handful of meal in her possession, and the last few drops of oil from her cruse. God rewarded her generosity by seeing to it that her barrel of grain and her cruse of oil were never empty while the famine lasted. The widow's cruse symbolises the hidden resources in the heart of a bereaved person. These need to be exploited so that the sad and bewildered mourner can begin a new life.

Margaret Torrie created a society to give help to the three million widows and widowers in Britain. Today there are Cruse groups in all the big towns, and these are ready to befriend and help their clients in much the same way as the other self-help groups. In 1970, Margaret Torrie augmented her good work by writing a minor classic called *Begin Again* (Dent, London). This little book is packed with useful information to help those who have lost their spouses. Many widowed people tend to feel that the full life is over for them, but, as the author has shown, this just is not so.

GROW

These letters are no acronym. The organisation claims to have a programme of growth to maturity, a system whereby people are led to identify their problems, and so learn how to deal with them. The term 'GROW' suggests to its members they must grow up and become mature people. This body was started by Con Keogh, a Catholic priest in Australia who found himself in a mental hospital suffering from a severe mental breakdown. He had electroplexy and all kinds of treatment, but nothing proved really helpful to him. In spite of all this, he did gradually recover, and was finally discharged from the hospital. He felt lost, lonely and far from well. He was desperately in need of help, and to secure this, he joined Alcoholics Anonymous, although alcoholic addiction was not his problem. In this society he found the support he needed. Realising that he was certainly not the only ex-patient from a psychiatric hospital to feel rejected and bewildered, he formed GROW to give them more appropriate treatment than that he had received from Alcoholics Anonymous.

A booklet called *Joannie's Story* published by GROW (GROW Magazine, 1975, vol 4.2) convinced me that this group could help the chronic patient who was defeating orthodox psychiatry. Joannie's was a chronic case of schizophrenia being cared for in a psychiatric ward. After many years of illness, she was considered hopeless. GROW took her over. No sudden miracle occurred, it took them five years to rehabilitate her, but cure her they did. She is now an attractive middle-aged woman, earning her own living and standing on her own feet.

The two essential features of GROW are that their groups

are able to offer tender loving care in almost unlimited quantities, and secondly, that they work along a structured programme. Small groups of about ten people meet on a regular basis every week, and the session of two hours follows a routine conducted by a leader. The leader, a more experienced GROW member, changes each week. The whole procedure is supervised and encouraged by a senior GROW member who has worked with the movement for some years, and is able to help if the group runs into difficulties. Such a person will be responsible for more than one group. Problems are discussed; for instance a member may reveal some of the difficulties he has run into, and indicate how he has tried to deal with them. In all this, confidentiality is essential, and group members are reminded of this. They are also encouraged to befriend each other between meetings by having coffee together or by telephoning each other.

There are religious overtones to these gatherings, but this should not deter non-believers from joining a group. Religion will not be thrust at them, and they will find themselves made most welcome. They can sit as observers for as long as they want; there is never any compulsion to speak or play an active role. For many, it is a long hard road back to normality, and on such a journey, people need a map. GROW provides just the guide that is needed in the form of the twelve steps to recovery. Carefully designed steps can make the steepest climb possible.

While GROW employs its own methods to help people, it is prepared to co-operate fully with the professionals. This is important as their knowledge and expertise is sometimes needed. I consider GROW to be a new and exciting idea to help those who have fallen victim to long-standing forms of mental illness. GROW has been working for many years in Australasia, some parts of the USA and throughout the republic of Ireland, but has only recently been started in Britain.

IN CONCLUSION

Mental depression is a very complex problem. It is made up of several syndromes and the treatment varies from one case to another. Man is a resilient creature, and most of us manage to work our way through the common everyday worries that afflict us. Science has made some very useful discoveries, and tools are now available with which to treat the most severe cases. Better drugs are on the way, and an increased understanding of the mechanism is being evolved.

For the vast group of sufferers who lie between the two extremes, of normal everyday depressions on the one hand, and the most severe forms of melancholia on the other, the solution to their problems may lie in wise counselling from professionals, or by being a member of some group. Tender loving care is a potent remedy. Some people will need a mixture of both counselling and drug therapy.

Those who have made a good recovery and are back to normal have perhaps one big responsibility, and that is to lend a hand to help others who are still wallowing in the slough of despond. Like the quality of mercy, the help given by those who have recovered to those who are still ill, is twice blessed, it blesseth him that gives and him that takes. The ideal aimed at by all treatment, is to get the patient back to normal without any need to rely on either drugs or doctors.

8
Résumé

Most depressed people are lacking in powers of concentration. If you are depressed and have managed to read through this book, you have done well, but you have probably largely forgotten most of what you have read. Because of this, I am going to summarise what has been said. Repetition does no harm; you may even want to go over the résumé more than once, until your recovery is complete.

The first thing to appreciate is that depression is a treatable illness, and no matter how convinced you feel that your condition is hopeless, give your adviser, and the treatment you are having, time to be effective. An old Quaker saying is 'think it possible you may be wrong'. However bad you feel and however sure you are that the treatment is going to be useless, do take the experts' advice.

If therapy consists of counselling, it may be some time before you have sorted out your problems. It is always unpleasant to face up to and accept personal defects. It is embarrassing to have to strip off one's clothes for a medical examination; it can be even more unpleasant to undress in a psychological sense. Fortunately most depressed people have an inferiority complex, and if they can be truly honest with themselves, they will find that they are far nicer people that they thought they were. Don't forget that we all have a few skeletons in the cupboard, and over the course of a lifetime, we all realise we have made the most stupid mistakes. We have created situations we deeply regret, and which are quite painful to recall, but to recall them may be necessary. One can only afford to forget the things one dares to remember. The worry or the conscience reaction can however, be spurious. A peccadillo of the past that suddenly intrudes itself into consciousness and becomes an obsession is likely to be unrealistic. It is probably a symptom of endogenous depression and will disappear once physical treatment has been instituted.

If the treatment consists of drug therapy, it will be a week or ten days before there is any improvement, and perhaps six weeks before the clouds have completely gone. Don't forget that during the early days of recovery, mood swings may well increase in intensity, and this can be most disconcerting when time and again hope of improvement is dashed by yet another swing of depression. You must keep on reminding yourself that these swings of mood are a good sign, as they indicate that the depression is on the way out. This phase soon passes, and normality will gradually become a permanent state of affairs. Depression is such a wretched experience, when the mood has passed, the feeling of relief is considerable. To be a normal person again can be compared to sunshine emerging after a prolonged shower. This change may seem impossible when you are ill, but it will come.

During the days of recovery, your spouse can be most useful, and you must take advantage of him or her. Work out a daily routine together, and then try to stick to it. The rules can be quite simple. Don't just lie in bed; keep reasonably active. Some people can do remarkable things, even at the nadir of depression. There are those who are helped by painting or drawing, and their pictures can, in a very graphic way, express just how they feel. Others do the same by writing poetry. One severely physically disabled woman became profoundly depressed after the death of her husband who had done so much for her. During her illness she actually learned to drive a specially-adapted car, so as to retain her mobility, and to gain a sense of independence.

Physical exercise is important, but it must not be overdone. Try to take a walk each day, and gradually increase the distance. Do a few odd jobs in the kitchen or garden. Any practical work of this kind gives a sense of achievement.

Mental activity is also important, and jigsaw puzzles and crosswords can be useful.

Eat sensibly and make sure you have good wholesome food with plenty of fresh fruit and vegetables. Most melancholics lose weight because they just cannot be bothered to prepare proper meals, or to sit down and eat an orderly meal. It is here that a routine helps. A few depressed people eat too much and put on weight. Such folk should have low calorie meals at regular intervals, and nibbling between them must be avoided. Alcohol is not a good idea. It often does not mix well with the drugs which have been prescribed, and if it does help to banish the low moods, it can be dangerous as the victim will then be in danger of drinking to excess. A course of Vitamin B tablets can do no harm, and may well do good to those who have been existing on a meagre diet.

Personal hygiene is important. The unshaven man who sees himself in a mirror is likely to be even more depressed by his appearance, and the same thing applies to the woman who has neglected her make-up. A visit to a hairdresser can greatly help such a person. It is important to bath regularly in spite of that awful feeling of exhaustion, and pay proper attention to your clothes. Keep regular hours. Go to bed at a sensible time, neither too early nor too late. Insomnia is usually cleared up by the appropriate dosage of anti-depressant drugs.

Most of these drugs have some unpleasant side effects. If you are upset by them, see your doctor and tell him how you feel. He may well change the drugs or alter the dosage, but you must not change the routine without his permission. You must stick to the treatment. The side effects will pass, and are worth putting up with to secure a complete recovery – after all, it is not unusual for a patient to feel worse before he feels better. A surgical operation may produce discomfort until the wound has healed, but time is the great healer.

Don't make any important decisions while you are feeling low. Wait until you have recovered when things may look very different. Make sure that you return completely to normal, and don't be satisfied by being only eighty per cent well. Your spouse will help you to make this assessment.

If you are unlucky enough to suffer from recurrent episodes of depression, you may not be certain when to call in the doctor. Obviously you won't need help over the odd day of feeling down, but if the low moods persist for two weeks, it is time to seek help. It is foolish to struggle on your own when expert help will improve things quickly. Those liable to recurrent attacks may well derive considerable help from bodies such as GROW, where a form of group therapy is available. The depressed are sick people, and, like others who are ill, they need the support of their families and their doctors or some lay adviser.

Useful Addresses

Samaritans
Revd D. Evans
17 Uxbridge Road
Slough
Berkshire
SL1 1SN

MIND
22 Harley Street
London
W1N 2ED

Depressives Associated
PO Box 5
Castle Town
Portland
Dorset
DT5 1BQ

Manic-Depressives Fellowship
51 Sheen Road
Richmond-on-Thames
Surrey
TW9 1YQ

Cruse
126 Sheen Road
Richmond-on-Thames
Surrey
TW3 1UR

GROW
Great Britain:
2 Tynemouth Street
Fulham
London
SW6 2QR

Ireland:
11 Liberty Street
Cork

Index